Exploring Limestone Landscapes of the Burren and the Gort Lowlands

A guide for walkers, cyclists and motorists

by
Mike Simms

Exploring the Limestone Landscapes of the Burren and the Gort Lowlands: A guide for walkers, cyclists and motorists.

Published by Mike Simms, Eden House, Belfast BT8 8JY

First Edition 2001
This Revised Edition 2006

Printed and bound by The Universities Press (Belfast) Ltd.

Acknowledgements
Many thanks to Tony Boycott, Andy Farrant, Graham Mullan, Matthew Parkes, Hugh Prudden and Alison Muir who helped in the preparation of this guide.

WARNING: It is inadvisable to enter any cave passages, other than those of commercial show caves, except under the supervision of experienced cavers. Furthermore, some of the surface terrain may be difficult, particularly in poor weather. Anyone embarking on these excursions, or entering any caves mentioned, does so entirely at their own risk. Mention in this guide does not imply a public right of way.

ISBN 0-9540892-1-9

CONTENTS

Front cover: Rinnenkarren (solution runnels) on sloping limestone pavement, Clooncoose, eastern Burren.

Back cover: Black Turlough Moss (*Cinclidotus fontinaloides*) on seasonally drowned boulders at Coole Lough, near Gort.

About this guide

The Burren is a remarkable area justly famous for its limestone scenery, the abundance and diversity of its archaeological monuments, and the richness of its flora. Many books have been written about this area, with new ones appearing each year. Some cover specific topics, such as flowers, lichens, agriculture and archaeology, but many others provide no more than a superficial treatment of each aspect. This is especially true of the stunning limestone landscape, despite it being the dominant feature of the area. Although the caves have been well described in several books, these are aimed mainly at cavers and there is little literature available to explain the surface, and underground, landscape to the ordinary visitor. This book, extensively revised from the previous edition published in 2001, addresses this shortcoming by explaining landscape features passed on popular routes across the Burren. The Burren is well known to tourists but the Gort lowlands to the east form a more subdued limestone landscape which is less often visited or written about. Nonetheless, it is a fascinating area which complements, and contrasts with, the Burren landscape. Anyone with an interest in the limestone landscapes of Ireland should visit the Gort area, and hence an excursion covering some of the main sites has been included here.

The sketch maps for each excursion, grouped together near the middle of this booklet, are intended only to give an indication of site locations. Not all of the roads and landmarks are indicated and so visitors are strongly advised to consult larger scale maps during their travels. The Ordnance Survey *Discovery Series* 1:50,000 sheets 51 (most of the Burren) and 52 (the extreme eastern Burren and the Gort lowlands) cover almost the entire area; grid references cited in this guide are from those maps. Tim Robinson's *Folding Landscapes* map of the Burren is also ideal for all but the Gort excursion and has many of the sites specifically marked. Although most of the sites in this guide are adjacent to, or at least visible from, roads and tracks, many are on private land. **The wishes of landowners and tenants must be respected**. Remember that **mention in this guide does not imply a public right of way**. Details of parking are indicated by a **P** at the end of each stop; its absence indicates that parking may be difficult. Even some of the smallest roads are in constant use so **do not block any roads**.

Although most roads within the Burren and Gort area are relatively minor, the region is easily reached from the main population centres. Galway to the north and Shannon Airport and Limerick to the south are within an hour's drive of the Burren, with Dublin only about 3 hours away. There is plentiful accommodation in the area to suit all tastes although it can be in short supply during the summer and in September, during the Match-making Festival at Lisdoonvarna. Larger hotels are found around Lisdoonvarna and Ballyvaghan but there are many B&Bs across the Burren and Gort region. For those on a more limited budget there are hostels at Doolin, Roadford and Fanore.

Facing directly into the Atlantic, the region experiences constantly changing weather. With an average of 260 rain days per year, fine weather is never a certainty. However, at some excursion stops there may be more to see after prolonged or heavy rain. In flood some of the sinks (swallow holes) and risings (springs) can be an impressive sight while the turloughs (seasonal lakes) show a remarkable contrast between summer and winter. Coastal sites can also be spectacular during unsettled weather and the ferocity of some of the winter storms which hit the Burren coast almost defies belief. **Take care at all sites during or following wet weather, since the bare rocks can be very slippery. EXTREME CARE should be taken at coastal sites in even mildly unsettled conditions - never take risks with the sea.**

Some technical terms have had to be used in this book but all are explained in the introductory sections. To help you refer back to these explanations these technical terms have been highlighted in **colour** where they are immediately followed, or preceded, by their explanation, and there is an index and glossary of these terms at the end of the book.

Why explore the Burren and Gort area?

The Burren is one of the most distinctive and best known landscape regions in Ireland and every year is visited by many thousands of people from all over the world. Even from the comfort of a car or coach the stark beauty, or some might call it bleakness, of the Burren, which literally means 'a rocky place', is very evident. For those venturing further from the road the Burren often seems like a vast, barely explored wilderness remote from the trappings of modern life. Despite the huge number of visitors, the area rarely seems crowded and it is easy to find solitude whilst walking the hills or green roads. To the east the Gort lowlands appear less remote and more like other agricultural areas of Ireland. But this belies its remarkable secrets. During the summer the gently rolling landscape is dotted with shallow lakes, seemingly unconnected lengths of sluggish river emerging from vast springs only to vanish underground again, and grassy glades strewn with moss-blackened boulders. During summer the landscape sleeps, but the winter rains bring it to life again and there is a dramatic transformation. The lakes expand, the rivers become dark swirling torrents, and the grassy glades and their blackened boulders are engulfed by water pouring from beneath the ground to form temporary lakes, or turloughs.

While the uncrowded nature of the Burren and Gort lowlands is true of many parts of rural Ireland, the landscape here is unique. The vast expanses of grey fissured rock, rising to cliffed and terraced hills in the Burren, might seem an unusual sight in a country renowned for its rolling green landscape, while the weird seasonal lakes and disappearing rivers of the Gort lowlands have an air of mystery about them. But all of these features are due to the dominant rock type in this area - limestone. Most rock types are removed slowly by mechanical erosion, usually by water breaking it into smaller particles which are then swept away. But limestone is different. Even though the limestone here is hard and resistant to erosion, like all limestones it has the rather peculiar property of dissolving in weakly acidic water, such as rain, to form what is called a **karst** landscape (named after a region of Slovenia where this type of landscape is well developed). Water percolates slowly through cracks in many types of rock, but only in limestone are these cracks widened by solution. Eventually they become large enough to engulf all of the water flowing across the surface and, for this reason, karst scenery is characterised by a lack of surface drainage. Some of these solutionally widened fractures may become large enough for us to explore; we call them cave passages.

Many features of karst landscapes are typified by the Burren and the Gort lowlands and can be seen on the excursions described later in this book. Indeed, this is an internationally important karst area and the finest in Ireland. The sinking streams, springs, and fissured limestone pavements are some of the most obvious results of limestone dissolution, but this is not the only process that has been important in creating the stark landscape of the Burren. During the past two million years or so much of Ireland was covered several times by thick ice sheets and glaciers. The most recent glaciation, which ended only about 14,000 years ago, scraped away much of the earlier soil and shale cover to leave vast areas of exposed limestone. These bare surfaces have since developed into the stunning limestone pavements for which the Burren is so famous. For this reason the Burren is often referred to as a **glaciokarst** landscape, since without the bulldozing effect of the ice sheets much of the Burren's character could not have developed.

What little soil cover once remained here, or that formed since the ice retreated, has largely disappeared, washed down the solutionally widened fissures. The scarcity of thick soils, and of surface water, across large areas of the Burren has profoundly influenced the plants that grow here. Indeed, Cromwell's surveyor Ludlow described the region as a "savage land, yielding neither water enough to drown a man, nor a tree to hang him, nor soil enough to bury" - an apt, if macabre, description of a classic karst landscape. But not all of the region is of bare rock. In parts of the Burren and Gort area the glaciers dumped masses of **boulder clay**, a chaotic jumble of 'ice-bulldozed' rock fragments, soil and clay. The valley floors and lower slopes of the Burren are often covered with this boulder clay, which consequently forms more intensively farmed areas. Further east thin patches and small rounded hills, or drumlins, of boulder clay occur scattered across the Gort lowlands. This boulder clay has partly blocked many of the underground drainage channels, contributing to the sometimes extensive flooding in winter following heavy rain.

The boundaries of the Burren and Gort lowlands

Much of the Burren comprises uplands which rise to 100-150 metres in the south, about 300 metres in the north, and a maximum of 344 metres on the sedge-covered slopes of Slieve Elva. The only significant areas of lowland, below 50 metres, within the Burren are a narrow coastal strip to the west and two valleys extending inland for several kilometres south from Ballyvaghan and Bell Harbour. The physical boundaries of the Burren are fairly easy to define. To the west and north the uplands fall steeply to the coast while the eastern scarp falls just as steeply onto the adjacent Gort lowlands, which seldom rise above 30 metres. The southern edge of the Burren can be drawn where the gentle southerly dip of the limestone carries it beneath the overlying shales along an irregular line running from Doolin, through Lisdoonvarna and Kilfenora, to Corofin **(see Figure 1)**.

Although the Burren is dominated by limestone, there are two substantial areas of the overlying shale **(see Figure 3)** that have survived erosion and still extend north across the limestone beneath. These are the Knockauns Mountain and Slieve Elva ridges and, to the east, the Poulacapple ridge **(see Excursion maps 1 and 2)**. Their damp sedge-covered slopes contrast strikingly with the freely draining limestone below. The boundary between the two is easily recognised by the change in vegetation and by the disappearance of small surface streams as they sink underground on reaching the limestone.

The Gort lowlands to the east form a striking contrast, rarely rising more than 30

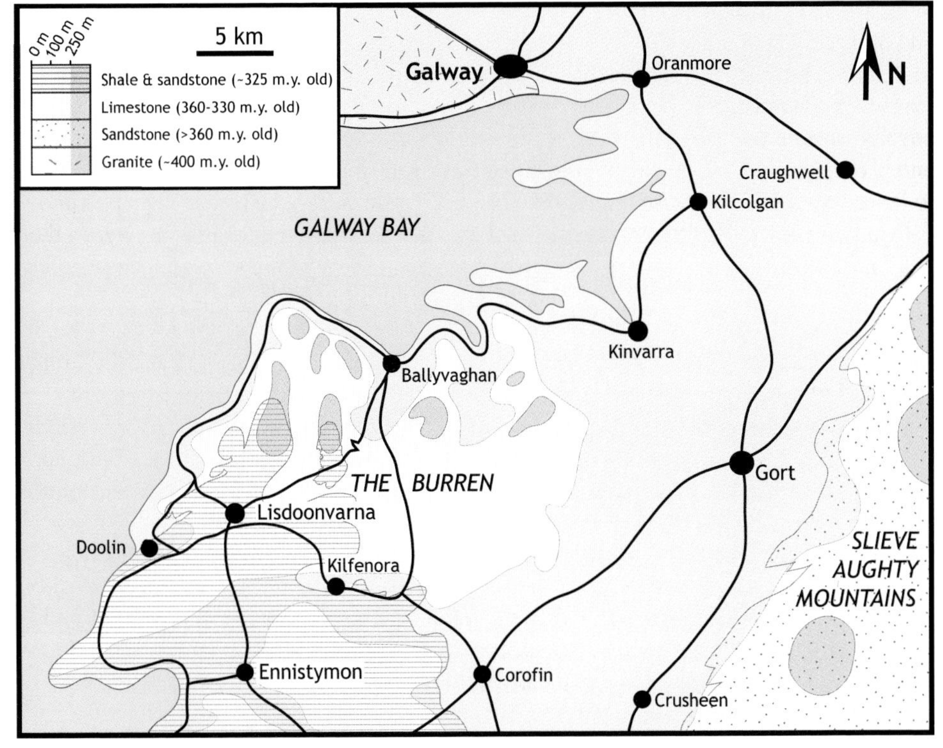

Figure 1. *General map of the Burren, Gort and Galway Bay area.*

metres above sea level, but they are rather more difficult to define. Their eastern margin is defined by the foot of the Slieve Aughty Mountains while the western boundary can be drawn along the Burren's eastern scarp in the south **(see Figure 2)** and the shores of Galway Bay in the north. The northern and southern margins of the lowlands are perhaps loosely defined by Craughwell in the north and Crusheen in the south **(Figure 1)**.

The rocks and their story

The geology of the Burren and Gort lowlands is actually very simple since there are really only two main rock types that we will see. These are the hard, grey, Carboniferous Limestone below and the dark grey to black, often iron-stained, Clare Shales (**shale** is a thinly-layered mudstone) above. Both were deposited during the **Carboniferous** Period, between about 360 and 320 million years ago. Originally they formed horizontal layers but they now dip gently southwards over most of the region. This dip is most obvious along the coast, with the limestone finally disappearing beneath the overlying shale near Doolin **(see Stop D1)**. More than 450 metres of the Carboniferous Limestone are exposed on the Burren itself, but the base lies several hundred metres lower still. These lower beds come to the surface on the east side of the Gort lowlands. The lowest beds seen on the Burren include dolomitic limestones (**dolomite** is a mineral composed of

Figure 2. *View from Mullagh More and the eastern scarp of the Burren hills, across the lake-strewn limestone 'corrosion plain' of the Gort lowlands, to the distant sandstone ridge of the Slieve Aughty Mountains.*

magnesium calcium carbonate; it is slightly less soluble than **limestone**, which is fairly pure calcium carbonate). They weather black and are seen on the lower slopes of Black Head, hence its name. Above are massive grey limestones, which form the lower slopes in the northern part of the Burren, overlain by nine thick limestone beds separated by clay bands less than a metre thick. Together this alternation of thick limestone and thin clay beds gives many of the Burren hills their distinctive terraced appearance. At the top of the limestone succession, forming the gentle slopes above the top terrace, are fossiliferous grey limestones with many nodules of **chert** (an impure form of flint). Chert is insoluble and so these nodules often protrude from weathered limestone surfaces **(see inside front cover)**. The silica of which it is made was derived from countless sponge spicules and microscopic radiolaria which lived in the tropical Carboniferous sea.

Above the limestone is the other main rock type of the Burren region; the black, impermeable, Clare Shales. They form the high ground of Poulacapple and Slieve Elva, and the slopes rising to the south of the Burren limestone outcrop. They are well exposed in the cliffs on the south side of Doolin Bay. Higher beds with more sandstones are superbly exposed, though rather inaccessible for close inspection, in the Cliffs of Moher. All of these sandstones and mudstones were deposited in mid-Carboniferous times, about 325 million years ago. The Clare Shales and overlying sandstones are impermeable and insoluble, and hence form the catchment of many streams which flow onto the limestone. The shales weather to an often waterlogged, heavy, grey clay which forms only poor,

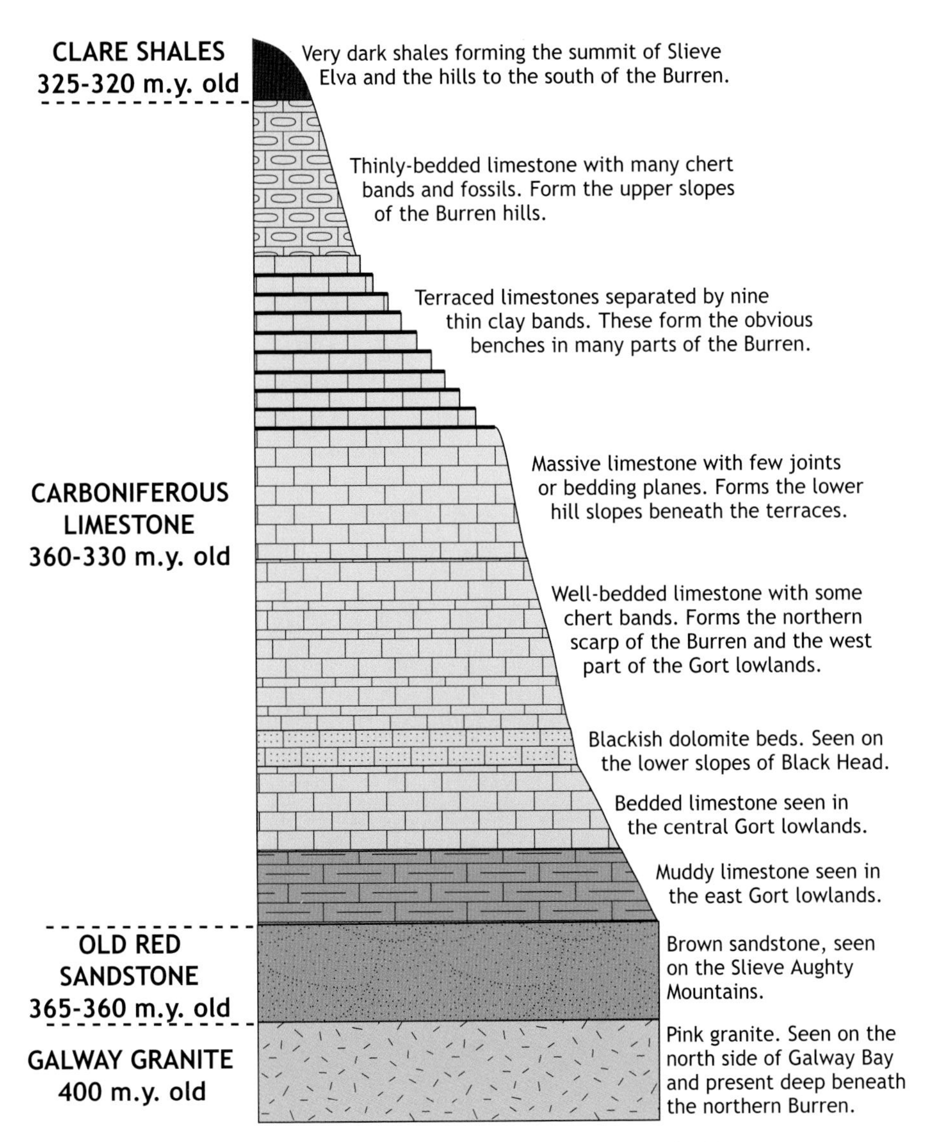

Figure 3. *Vertical section through the rocks beneath the Burren and the Gort lowlands (not to scale).*

sedge-covered pasture. However, these thick, rather acidic soils are ideal for conifers, with which the shale cap of both Slieve Elva and Poulacapple have been extensively planted.

Other rocks, of different types and ages, come to the surface in areas adjacent to the Burren and Gort lowlands and are occasionally seen here as ice-transported fragments, or erratics. These other rocks are important for understanding how the landscape has developed and reached its present form. Beneath the Carboniferous Limestone are brown sandstones and pebble beds of the Old Red Sandstone (of **Devonian** age, about 365 million years old). These rocks lie deep beneath the Burren but they come to the surface in the Slieve Aughty Mountains, to the east of the Gort lowlands. Up-folded layers have been exposed here as the overlying limestone has been eroded away. The Old Red Sandstone is insoluble and relatively impermeable, and so the Slieve Aughty Mountains form the main catchment for rivers draining west on to the Gort lowlands. As such they have been very important in forming some of the karst features found there.

To the north of the Burren lies the remarkably straight northern shore of Galway Bay, which is formed of Galway Granite. This granite originated as molten rock which solidified deep beneath the surface about 400 million years ago. The granite probably extends southwards deep beneath the northern part of the Burren. Pebbles, and even large boulders, of Galway Granite are found scattered across the surface of the Burren and show that ice movement was from the north during the last million years or so. Still further north is the ancient (up to 750 million years old) schist, quartzite and marble of Connemara. These rocks from Galway and Connemara have little direct bearing on the Burren landscape but are very distinctive and occasionally turn up as **erratics**. As such they provide evidence for the direction of ice movement during the Ice Age.

Ancient rivers, tropical seas and Earth movements

The three main rock types which underlie this area, the Old Red Sandstone, Carboniferous Limestone and Clare Shales, represent enormous changes in the environment over about 50 million years. Sandstones and pebble beds in the Old Red Sandstone were deposited by rivers flowing from an ancient mountain chain onto a flood plain. The hills of Connemara and Mayo to the north are perhaps the eroded stumps of some of these ancient mountains. The only fossils found in these rocks are occasional small pieces of plant debris.

In early Carboniferous times, around 360 to 340 million years ago, sea level rose slowly to flood across these plains. Ireland lay roughly on the Equator and, in the warm tropical seas, calcium carbonate was deposited to form limestone. Fossils of corals and **brachiopods** (a type of shellfish; **see Figure 4**) show that these limestones were deposited on a shallow sea floor. At first the limestone was diluted by mud brought down by the rivers. These muddy limestones lie immediately above the Old Red Sandstone and are

Figure 4. *Cross-sections through the shells of fossil brachiopods (of a type known as Productus) at Lackglass, on the Burren coast (see Stop D7). These are among the most common type of fossil found in the Carboniferous Limestone of the Burren and Gort area.*

found on the east side of the Gort lowlands. As sea level continued to rise, drowning more of the land, the influence of these rivers lessened until there was very little mud to dilute the limestone. These are the pure limestones found across the rest of the Gort lowlands and the Burren. Temporary falls in sea level exposed the newly deposited limestones to rain and weathering for a few thousand years and their surfaces became pock-marked by solution, just as on the limestone pavements we see today. These ancient pitted surfaces are called **palaeokarst**. As sea level rose again a thin clay layer was deposited over the palaeokarst before normal limestone deposition resumed **(see Figure 28)**. The effects of these minor fluctuations in sea level are seen in the Burren terraces which have been picked out by erosion. The same clay bands can be traced across to the Aran Islands in Galway Bay and even as far as the Yorkshire Dales and the Peak District in England, so we know that they were not due to just local changes in sea level.

There is a time gap of a few million years between the highest limestone and the lowest bed of the overlying Clare Shales. Very slow deposition during this time allowed fish teeth and scales to accumulate on the sea floor and become converted into phosphate minerals. Phosphate deposits up to 2 metres thick around the village of Roadford, near Doolin, were once quarried for fertiliser. The mudstones of the Clare Shales above were deposited in deep water off the mouth of a huge river delta. Shelly fossils are common only at a few levels, notably near the base of the Clare Shales, but show that it was mostly marine. However, other animals such as marine worms or snails, whose soft

Figure 5. *Bedding planes (horizontal) and joints (vertical) are clearly visible in the Carboniferous Limestone at Boodaun, on the coast near Doolin (see Stop D3). These breaks in the rock control many of the landscape features in the Burren.*

bodies were never preserved as fossils, have left innumerable sinuous trails across some of the sandstones and mudstones which lie above the Clare Shales. These are the famous Liscannor Flags which are quarried to the south of the Burren.

All of these rocks were originally deposited in a series of unbroken horizontal layers, one upon another. But around 290 million years ago there were major Earth movements caused by continental plates colliding. Across much of the Burren the originally horizontal limestone beds were tilted about 2° to the south-south-east. There are very few faults or folds, perhaps reflecting the solid foundation provided by the Galway Granite which lies beneath much of the northern Burren. To the east and south-east the limestone beds are more folded and faulted **(see Figure 11)**, perhaps hinting at the limits of the buried Galway Granite. Folding is best seen on Mullagh More, but elsewhere in the south-eastern Burren and the Gort lowlands dips on the limestone may be quite steep.

The limestone is broken by nearly horizontal fractures formed by **bedding-planes**, which separate the original layers in which the limestone was deposited, and by vertical fractures, known as **joints**, which formed during ancient Earth movements **(see Figure 5)**. The dominant joints are orientated almost north-south (196°) with a second set running east-west (270°). Their spacing, so superbly displayed on the limestone pavements **(see Figure 7)**, varies from several metres to less than a metre. Occasionally, opposing faces of fractures or bedding planes show linear grooves and ridges, often associated with white calcite veins. These scratches, known as **slickensides (see Figure 27)**, formed as rock surfaces moved past each other along a **fault**, marking the epicentre of an ancient earthquake.

The surface landscape

The surface landscape of this area has formed from the interaction of ice and water with the different rocks over at least the last million years or so. The underlying influence of the geology on weathering and erosion is seen most clearly in features such as the limestone terraces and the regular fractures on the limestone pavements.

The glacial legacy

Over the past two million years the entire region has been buried, probably several times, by a slowly moving ice sheet which may have been several hundred metres thick. The most recent glaciation ended only about 14,000 years ago. It scraped bare large areas of the limestone surface and rounded off north-facing slopes **(see Figure 20)**. Elsewhere it plucked blocks from south-facing crags and deposited chaotic masses of boulder clay in hollows and in the lee of some of the hills. Boulder clay often provides the only significant soil cover on the limestone surface. As the ice moved across the landscape it gouged deep scratches, or **glacial striae**, into the rock surface beneath (unlike **slickensides** found on faults, which are sandwiched between two solid masses of rock, these glacial scratches are found only on exposed rock surfaces or beneath boulder clay). On the bare limestone surfaces these striations have long since weathered away but those buried by boulder clay have been protected and can now be seen where the boulder clay is stripped back by the sea **(see Figure 6)**. The orientation of these glacial striations show that the most

Figure 6. *Glacially striated limestone exposed as the overlying boulder clay is eroded away on the shore at Poulcraveen (Stop D4).*

recent ice advance was from the north-east. However, occasional erratics of granite, schist and quartzite from north of Galway Bay suggest that an earlier ice advance came from the north or north-west. Limestone pavements are not found beneath areas of thick boulder clay so it is likely that many of the small-scale karst features, and at least some of the active stream sinks and caves on the Burren, probably have formed since the last glaciation. However, the larger karst landforms are too deep and extensive to have formed only in the last few thousand years. They include long and complex cave systems, such as Poulnagollum **(Stop F8)**; enormous closed depressions, such as at Carran **(Stop C10)**; and especially the Gort lowlands with its complex subterranean drainage and network of surface lakes and turloughs **(Excursion G)**. All of these must have started to form long before the last glacial episode, perhaps even before any of the glacial activity of the last two million years, although glacial erosion and deposition has greatly modified them since. Because of this interplay between glaciation and karstification, the karst landscape of the Burren is often referred to as **glaciokarst**. It is only through the glacial stripping of the shale and soil that once covered the limestone that the extensive limestone pavements of the Burren and Gort lowlands have been able to develop.

Solution at the surface

The small-scale features developed on bare limestone surfaces by the effects of rainfall are as diverse as the larger-scale landscape and include far more than just the familiar clints and grikes. The limestone's low porosity does not allow rainwater to soak in and

Figure 7. *Limestone pavement on Mullagh More, in the south-east Burren. Scraped bare by glaciation solution has since picked out the vertical fractures (joints) to form grikes (the fissures), which are separated by clints (the blocks in between). Rillenkarren (solution flutes) and a small kamenitza (solution pan) are visible in the foreground to left and right respectively.*

so solution pans, or **kamenitzas**, often develop on bare limestone surfaces **(see Figures 7 and 18)**. However, joints are slowly widened by percolating water to form **grikes**, with intervening blocks of limestone termed **clints**; this is the classic form of limestone pavement **(see Figure 7)**. Clint size depends upon joint spacing, with some covering many square metres in area. On sloping limestone surfaces, such as occur in parts of the south-east Burren and the Gort lowlands, rainwater drains down slope to form sub-parallel series of runnels. Larger runnels which become deeper and wider down slope are termed **rinnenkarren**, or solution runnels **(see front cover)**; smaller ones on steeper slopes, and with depth and width remaining fairly constant down slope, are called **rillenkarren** or solution flutes **(see Figure 7)**. Where drainage has been concentrated onto a particular point a circular depression, known as a **doline**, may develop **(see Figure 8)**; larger, more irregular, examples are known as **uvalas (see Figure 24)**. Some are only a metre or two deep and a few metres across but others in the Burren, such as the Carran depression **(Stop C10)**, may be several tens of metres deep and cover several square kilometres, reflecting a complex history of karstification and glacial modification. On the Gort lowlands, where the regional water table lies at relatively shallow depth, many of these large depressions are permanent lakes. Others are flooded only when water is unable to drain away underground fast enough, such as often occurs in winter. These are the **turloughs**, or 'seasonal lakes' **(see Figures 22, and 35 to 37)**, which are such a remarkable element of the karst landscape of western Ireland. Even in summer, when they are dry, turloughs are instantly recognisable from the presence of the Black Turlough Moss, *Cinclidotus fontinaloides*, which covers boulders, walls and bushes submerged by

Figure 8. *A closed depression, or doline, near Poulnabrone Dolmen (Stop B4). These are among the most characteristic features of karst landscapes. On any other rock type a depression like this would be water-filled, but on limestone the water can escape via an underground drainage route.*

winter flooding **(see back cover)**.

Dry valleys are another common feature of karst landscapes where most of the drainage is underground. In the Burren permanent surface streams are found only on the Clare Shales or in a few places on the limestone where they flow over boulder clay, such as in the Caher and Rathborney river valleys **(stops E13 and E15)** and the floor of the Carran depression **(Stop C10)**. However, dry valleys and steep-sided gorges are fairly commonplace though many have no obvious relationship to the present surface drainage. At least some probably were carved out during the cold periods of the ice age when permafrost prevented summer meltwater from sinking underground and forced it to flow across the surface like a normal river. Among the most impressive of these gorges are near Ballynalackan Castle **(Stop A2)** and below Cahercommaun fort **(Stop C8)**.

The retreat of the last ice sheet about 14,000 years ago left many **erratic boulders** (so called because they have been carried by the ice beyond where they originated) scattered across the bare limestone surface. Usually they are of limestone but some are of Galway Granite or other rocks. Since then rainfall has slowly lowered the limestone surface by dissolution except where it is protected by these erratics, somewhat in the manner of an umbrella. These boulders now rest on pedestals whose height shows the thickness of limestone that has been removed from the surrounding surface by rainfall since the ice sheets melted **(see Figure 9)**.

Figure 9. *This erratic boulder at Poulsallagh (See Stops A4) was left behind as the last ice sheet retreated. By sheltering the limestone surface from rainfall, a pedestal has developed beneath the erratic as the exposed limestone surrounding it has been lowered by solutional weathering.*

On the coast a rather peculiar type of karst is found in a narrow zone affected by tides and waves. At low tide fretted, jagged or rounded pinnacles are exposed between shallow rock pools. Many of the pinnacles are encrusted with barnacles and mussels, while the large pools near low water are crowded with purple sea urchins (*Paracentrotus lividus*), each of which has excavated a small depression in which it lives **(Figure 10)**. But how have these pools and pinnacles developed? They cannot have been dissolved out by sea water because this is already saturated with carbonate. Strangely, these pits and pinnacles are absent from the darkest parts of caves which have been partly drowned by the sea, such as those on Doolin Point **(Stop D2)** and at Poulsallagh **(Stop A4)**, and this is a clue to how they have formed. In dimly lit parts of these caves the walls are covered with tiny sharp pinnacles which all point towards the light! These pinnacles are called **photokarren**, or **photokarst**. They form where microscopic algae, which live just a few micrometres below the rock surface but are dependant on light, etch the limestone in some places to leave narrow pinnacles in between. These same algae have a similar, though less directional, effect out on the shore. Animals, such as limpets and the purple sea urchins, then graze upon the algae with their rasping tongues or teeth. Together these animals and microscopic algae have created the jagged surfaces on the shore, together called **biokarst**, without any direct dissolution by the sea water.

Figure 10. Pinnacles and rock pools in the limestone exposed at low tide on Doolin Point (see Stop D2). Sometimes termed biokarst, they form through bioerosion by marine animals and plants, not through direct dissolution by sea water. The dark spots in the rock pool are sea urchins (Paracentrotus lividus).

Burren uplands vs. Gort lowlands: Why so different?

Both the Burren and the Gort lowlands are made largely of the same rock type, limestone, yet the landscapes of these two regions are strikingly different. Why is this? There is no evidence that the limestone in the lowlands was any weaker or more easily eroded than on the Burren, or that the lowlands were gouged out by more intense ice movements. But there is evidence that the limestone has been exposed to dissolution for much longer in the Gort lowlands than over most of the Burren uplands.

Beneath the surface of the Burren most cave passages are relatively small and closely related to the present landscape **(see Figures 13 and 16)**. In contrast, the gently undulating Gort lowlands are underlain by sections of enormous phreatic passage, sometimes more than 10 metres across **(see Figure 33)**, connecting various surface lakes, turloughs and rivers. These cave fragments represent parts of a vast ancient cave system now partly destroyed by surface lowering through dissolution and glacial erosion.

It is the geology that once again is the key to understanding the difference between these two areas. Many millions of years ago the limestone across the whole area would have been buried beneath a thick cover of the impermeable Clare Shales and so was protected from dissolution. However, the various rock layers were upfolded in the east, across the present Slieve Aughty Mountains **(see Figure 11)**, and so erosion uncovered the limestone here first and exposed it to dissolution. As erosion continued the Old Red

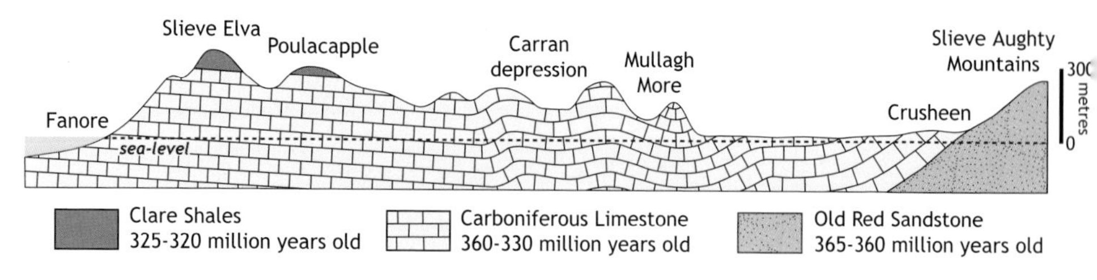

Figure 11. *East-West sketch section through the Burren and Gort lowlands, showing the relationship of the underlying rocks to the surface landscape (after P.W.Williams; see Ford and Williams 1989).*

Sandstone beneath was exposed, allowing large surface rivers to flow westwards onto the limestone **(see Excursion Map 3)**, where they sank to form the great cave passages found beneath the Gort lowlands. Over the last few million years the wet climate of western Ireland has actually removed limestone by dissolution faster than other rocks have been removed by erosion. On the Burren it is clear that the Clare Shales have protected the limestone beneath across large areas until relatively recently, so there has been far less time for dissolution to remove the limestone there. Indeed, a shale cap still remains on Slieve Elva and Poulacapple, and covers the limestone to the south of the Burren **(see Excursion Map 1)**, which accordingly is protected from dissolutional lowering for at least a little while longer. The location of hills in the Burren reflects the relative recency of this shale cover whereas to the east, on the Gort lowlands, the shale was eroded away so long ago that the gently folded limestone beds have been bevelled off by dissolution to form a remarkably flat 'corrosion plain'. However, the slow dissolution of the limestone which created the Gort lowlands is still operating today. Ultimately, perhaps in another 4 or 5 million years, these lowlands will extend west right across what is now the Burren!

Beneath the surface

The thick, pure limestones of the Burren and much of the Gort lowlands are ideal for the development of cave passages. However, direct rainfall onto the limestone is too dispersed to form large passages, which instead usually form where a stream flows from an impermeable catchment rock, such as shale or sandstone, onto the limestone. The point where the water passes underground is known as a **sink** (or **swallow hole**) and it finally re-emerges after its underground journey at a **rising** (or **resurgence** or **spring**).

Cave passages can develop both above the water table, in what is known as the vadose zone, or below it, in what is called the phreatic or saturated zone **(see Figure 12)**. They tend to be guided initially by pre-existing fractures, such as bedding planes and joints. Phreatic caves have a passage shape which is different from that of vadose caves, and these shapes can be used to tell us where the water table was when particular passages formed even long after they have dried up **(see Figure 12)**. Beneath the water table, in the **phreatic zone**, all cavities in the limestone are water-filled and so the limestone dissolves

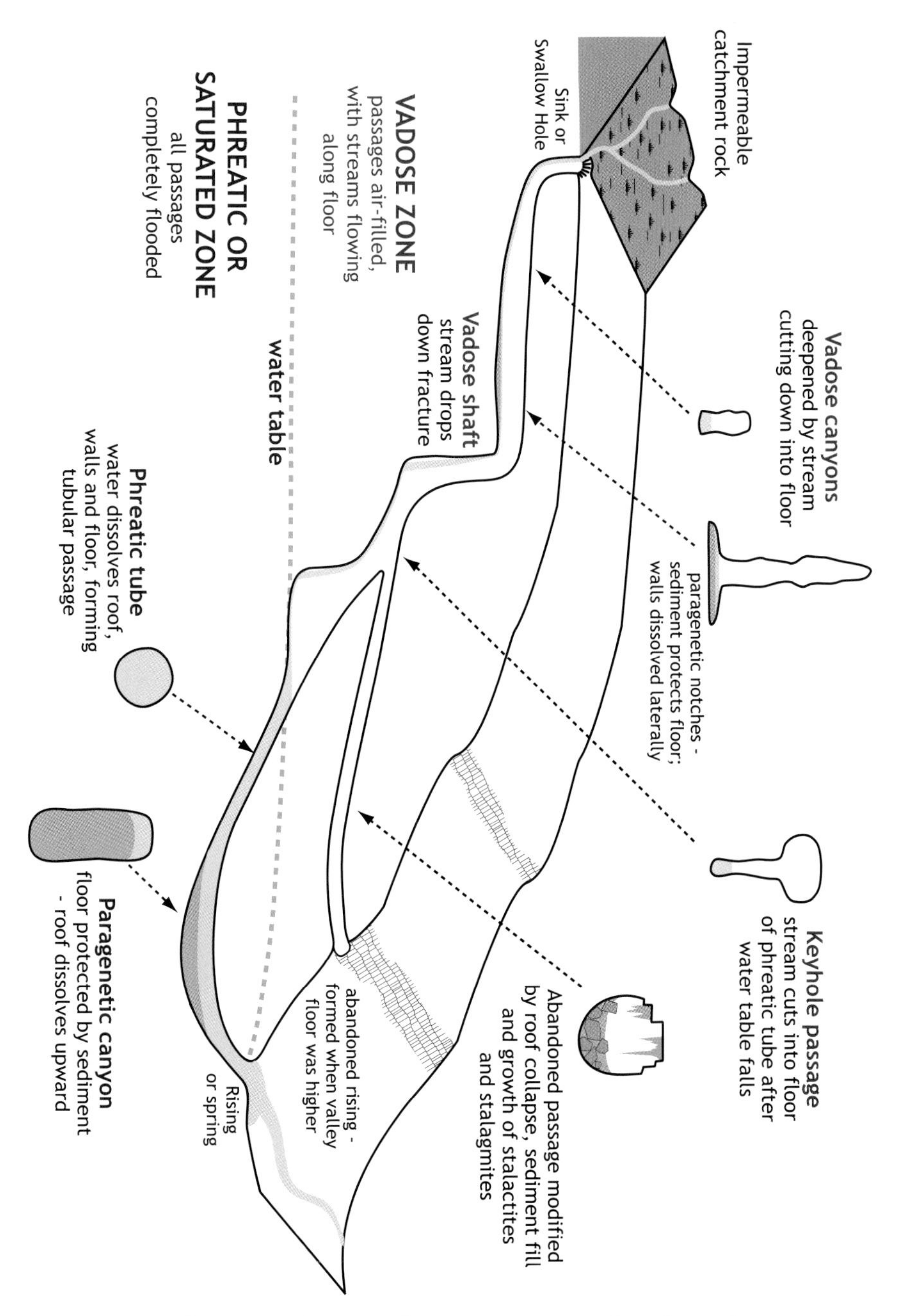

Figure 12. *Sketch section through a cave system to show the various passage shapes and their relationship to the position of the water table. Examples of most of these can be seen on the excursions.*

Figure 13. *Active vadose canyon with the stream cutting down into the floor, Doolin River Cave. The cascade entering from the roof is water leaking from the Aille River (see Stop E1), which flows above the cave near here. It marks the approximate position of the 'proto-cave' from which the present stream passage has cut downwards.*

Figure 14. *Paragenetic canyon from which the sediment has long since been flushed out, Oughtdarra. It developed from one of the tiny 'proto caves' on the bedding plane across the middle of the picture. Sediment deposited on the passage floor confined dissolution to the roof, forming a canyon which grew upwards from the original 'proto-cave'.*

in all directions to form passages with circular or elliptical cross sections. These are often known as **phreatic tubes**, or half-tubes where they are floored by an insoluble shale band **(see Figures 17 and 28)**. Water flow here follows the path of least resistance, even flowing uphill if necessary like water in the U-bend under the sink. In contrast, above the water table in the **vadose zone** water flows only in the lower part of the passage and always downhill, just like a surface stream. As a result it can only cut down into the floor and so forms a **vadose canyon (see Figure 13)**. Sometimes the stream may drop vertically down a fault or joint to form a **vadose shaft**. During a cave's history the water table may fall but water continues to flow along passages originally formed in the phreatic zone. Such passages are identified by their keyhole shape, with a **vadose trench** carved into the floor of a phreatic tube **(see Figure 16)**. However, there is another type of passage found in some Burren caves that formed in the phreatic zone yet has the appearance of a

Figure 15. Solutional scalloping of a limestone surface by flowing water. These scallops (3-4 cm long) show that the water flowed from left to right at a velocity of about one metre per second (about 2 mph).

vadose canyon. These develop where sediment (mud or sand) accumulates on the passage floor and protects it from dissolution, which instead is confined to the exposed limestone in the roof. Over time the roof slowly dissolves upwards as more sediment accumulates on the floor and a canyon-shaped passage, largely filled with sediment, is formed. If this sediment is later washed out the canyon shape of the passage is revealed. These are known as **paragenetic passages** and extend *upwards* from the level at which the cave originated, such as a bedding plane; in contrast a vadose canyon cuts *downwards* **(compare Figures 13 and 14)**. Paragenetic canyons can also be distinguished from vadose canyons by the presence of undulating ledges and notches along the walls **(see Figure 19)**. These ledges mark the depth of sediment in the passage at various stages of its development. Superficially similar ledges in vadose passages are sub-horizontal, rather than undulating.

As well as using cave passage shape to tell us about the former level of the water table, it is also easy to determine the direction and speed of water flow by looking for asymmetric, scoop-shaped hollows, called **scallops (see Figure 15)**, on passage walls. These form by dissolution in small eddies, with the steeper side facing downstream. Scallop size is a measure of the speed the water was flowing when they formed, with small scallops indicating faster flow than larger ones. A rough rule of thumb for calculating water flow (in metres per second) is to divide 3.5 by the mean length of the scallops in centimetres.

In section it is clear that many cave passages formed originally along bedding planes, producing wide, low, often meandering, passages **(see Figure 16)**. Where passages

Figure 16. *Stalactites, stalagmites and flowstone adorn Faunarooska Cave, beneath north-west Slieve Elva (Stop E10), and have been precipitated from carbonate-saturated water percolating down cracks in the rock. The original passage shape can still be seen, with a scalloped vadose trench incised into the floor of a low, wide phreatic passage formed on a bedding plane.*

were more strongly guided by vertical fractures in the limestone, straight stretches of passage are linked by sharp bends. Although many caves in this area still carry flowing water, abandoned passages are also common. These show that many of the caves have had a long and complex history during which they have been modified by abandonment, sediment infilling, reoccupation by flowing water and, ultimately, by collapse and destruction. Often these processes, particularly collapse, have obscured the original passage shape and scalloping on the walls, making interpretation more difficult. The age of the caves themselves remains poorly known though at least some are many hundreds of thousands of years old and must have started to form when the landscape was very different from today.

Rainwater percolating directly downwards from the bare limestone surface above rarely forms large passages, but it is important in forming **stalactites**, **stalagmites** and **flowstone** which are so conspicuous in many caves **(see Figure 16)**. This percolation water slowly dissolves calcite in the limestone through which it passes, only to redeposit it upon entering an air-filled cavity such as a cave passage. The ratio of Thorium and Uranium isotopes within these calcite formations can tell us how old they are and, since they form only in the vadose zone, can indicate when a phreatic passage was drained. They are also becoming an increasingly important source of information on past climate.

Figure 17. An ancient phreatic tube abandoned by a fall in the water table and now truncated by erosion, Aillwee Mountain.

Caves of the Burren uplands

Most of the known caves on the Burren are associated with stream sinks located along the shale edge around Slieve Elva **(Excursion F)**, Knockauns Mountain **(Excursion E)** and Poulacapple. Typically these sinks lead to narrow winding vadose canyons with only a gentle gradient; some remain only a few metres below the surface for hundreds of metres. In others the stream descends one or more vadose shafts, in one case reaching a depth of more than 180 metres **(see Stop E9/F4)**. Exploration of most Burren caves has ended at flooded passages perched on the relatively impermeable chert bands in the upper beds of the limestone, even though these lie some distance above sea level. Nonetheless, the water from some caves has been traced to submarine risings a short distance off the west coast of the Burren **(see stops D1, D3 and D12)**. Typical phreatic cave passages are relatively uncommon in the Burren. Most lie well away from the present shale margin and have long since been drained by a fall in the water table **(see Figure 17)**. The most extensive, and best known, phreatic passage in the Burren is in Aillwee Cave. It is typical of the phreatic passages known in the Burren in that it must have formed when the landscape was very different from what we see today. For a further explanation of how caves form, and are modified subsequently, Aillwee Cave **(Stop B1)** is well worth a visit.

Caves of the Gort lowlands

The Slieve Aughty Mountains form the main catchment for the Gort lowlands, with three major rivers draining from the impermeable Old Red Sandstone uplands to disappear underground at several large sinks along the edge of the limestone lowlands to the west **(see Excursion Map 3)**. This eastern outcrop of limestone, bent up against the Slieve Aughtys, was exposed to rain and sinking streams long before the protective shale cover was stripped from the Burren uplands further west. Hence the Gort lowlands, and the cave passages beneath, must be very much older than most of the karst features now seen on the Burren. However, subsequent weathering and glacial erosion has destroyed large sections of this ancient cave system while glacial deposits have partially blocked many parts of the surviving underground drainage. Over large areas of the Gort lowlands today the regional water table lies close to the surface and the karst drainage here is dominated by permanently flooded, and often very large (more than 10 metres across), phreatic cave passages. These drain westwards to major intertidal and submarine risings at Corranroo and Kinvarra **(Stop G13)**. Unlike most of the caves on the Burren, which can be explored easily by ordinary cavers, most of the passages beneath the Gort lowlands are permanently flooded and accessible only to divers, although there are a few notable exceptions **(see Stop G7)**. Only a few of these flooded passages have actually been explored although some have been followed by cave divers for hundreds of metres. They have found that tides affect the flow in these passages, even several kilometres inland!

A major investigation of the karst drainage of the area was undertaken following severe floods in 1995. By using dyes and other markers to trace the flow of water between sinks and risings, we now know a lot more about the underground drainage patterns. But until cave divers actually explore all of the passages we can do no more than guess about the exact route the water takes. Hence the straight dotted lines on Excursion Map 3 show only which sinks and risings have been proven (by dye tracing) to be connected; the precise route the water takes undoubtedly is far more complex.

Threatened landscapes?

The landscape we see today has developed over millions of years and continues to change almost imperceptibly through erosion and dissolution. The landscape also owes much to human activity over the last few millenia, with vegetation cleared or grazed, and rocks arranged into walls, tombs and dwellings. Indeed, it is these features that attract many visitors to the area in the first place. But in the last few decades the pace of change has accelerated and threatens to destroy many unique features of the area. The region must adapt to the times, but all too often the changes wrought are brutal and insensitive. Limestone pavements are ripped up with mechanical excavators; wild flower meadows are 'improved' and converted to monocultures; water courses and lakes are polluted by domestic refuse and agricultural runoff; and the inexorable spread of holiday homes increasingly blights the landscape. But tourists too contribute in their own small way to this slow degradation. Many accessible areas of limestone pavement on the Burren are littered with crude miniature 'dolmens' built of slabs ripped up from the surrounding pavement; erratic boulders have been toppled from pedestals on which they rested for perhaps 15,000 years; and of course there is the inevitable litter of cans, crisp packets and the like. Besieged from so many sides, one wonders on the state of this landscape in another few decades, let alone a few millennia. What will we leave to our descendants?

EXCURSION MAPS

These three sketch maps provide only an indication of the routes to be followed for the seven excursions, A to G, described in the following section. It is recommended that more detailed maps are also consulted. Details of parking, where possible, are indicated by a **P** at the end of each site description.

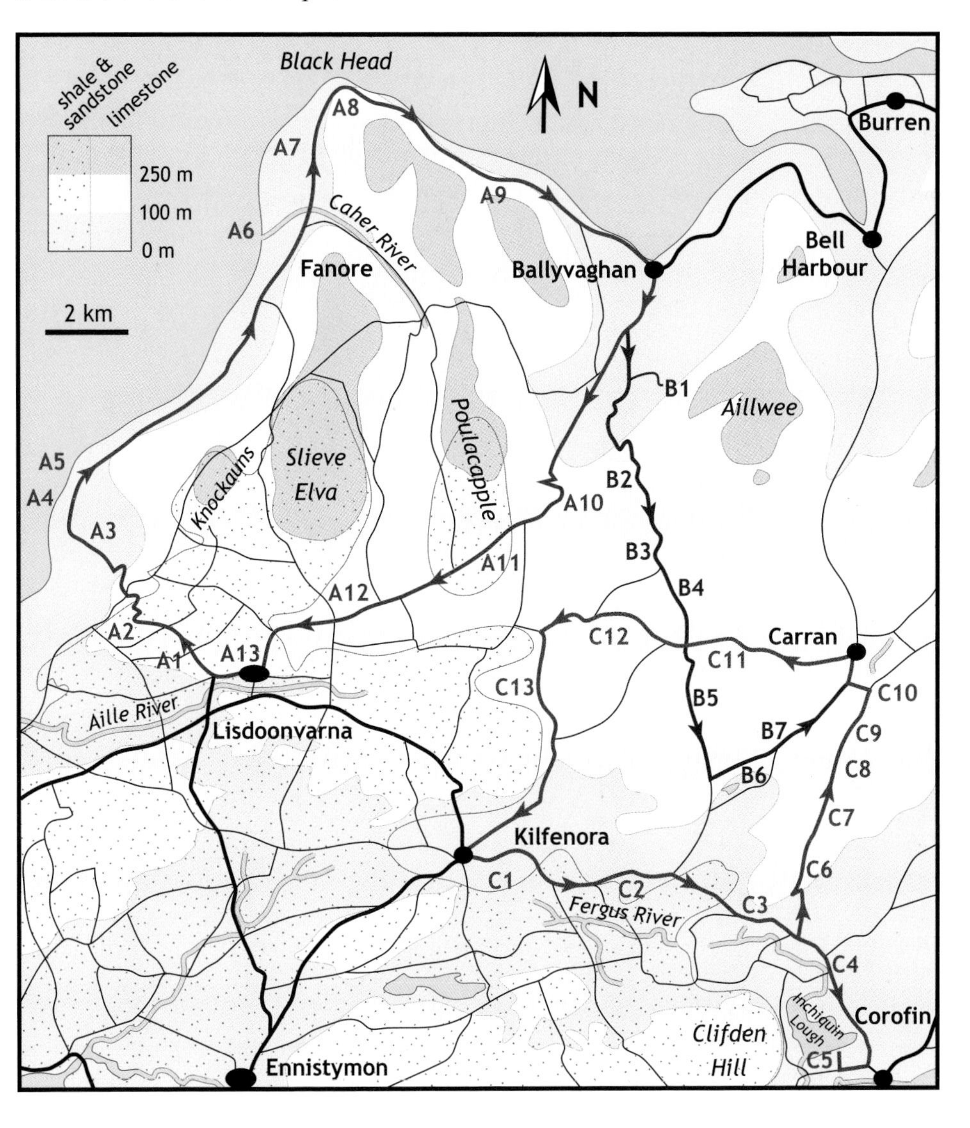

Map 1. *Sketch map for the main cycling/driving tours of the Burren centred on Lisdoonvarna and Kilfenora (Excursions A, B and C).*

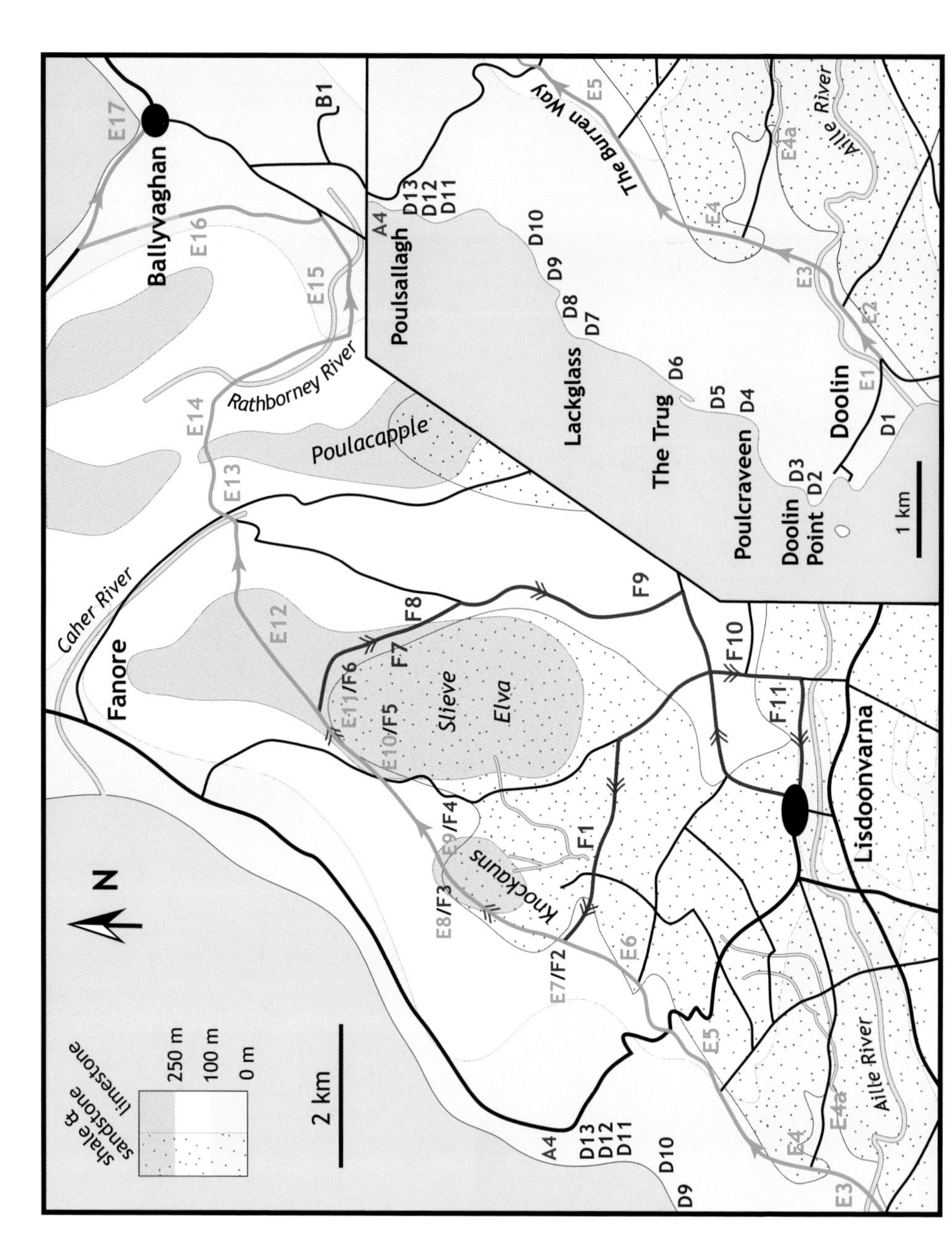

Map 2. *Sketch maps for the main walking tours of the Burren: The Burren Way (Excursion E), the Slieve Elva Circuit (Excursion F), and the Doolin-Poulsallagh coast walk (Inset: Excursion D).*

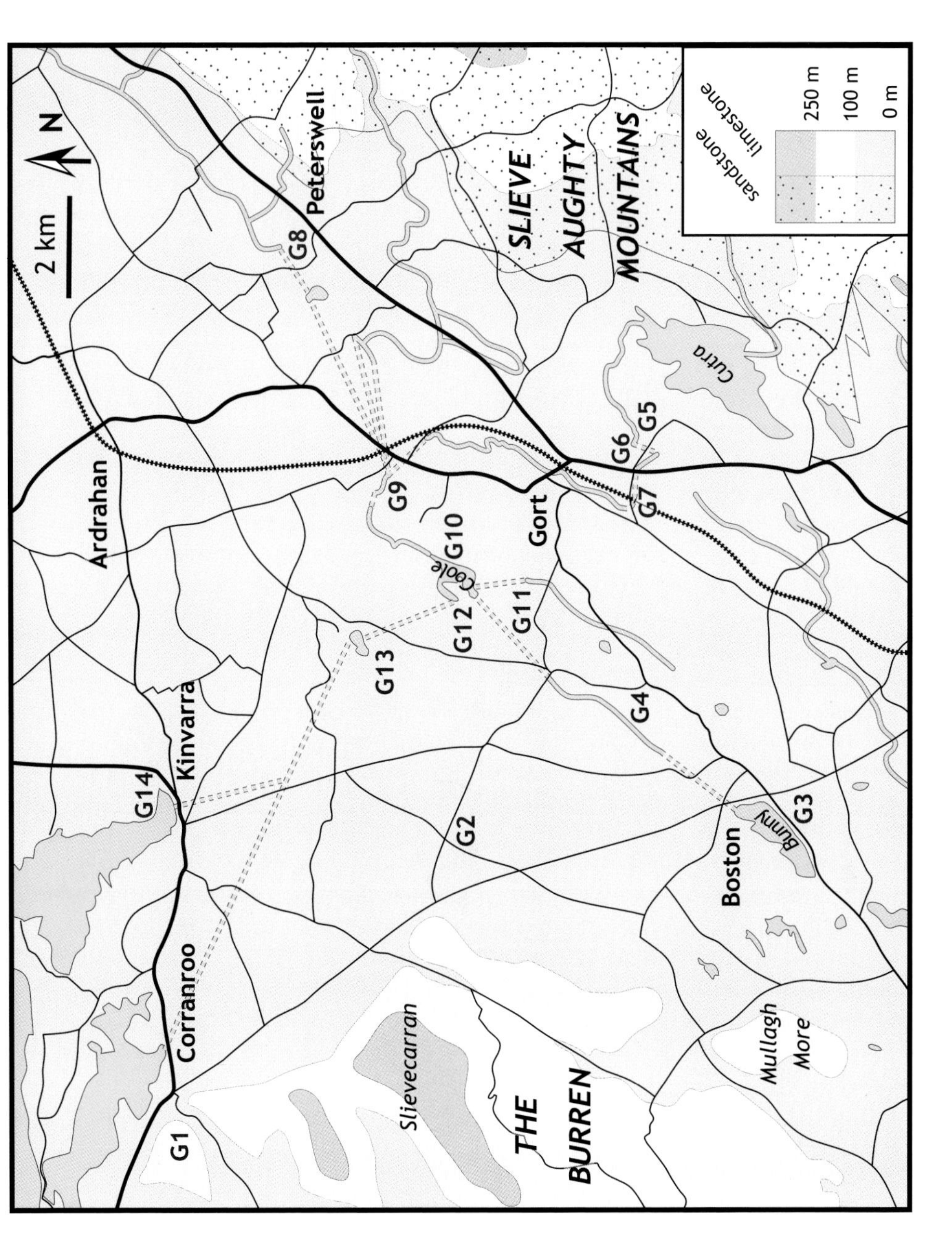

Map 3. *Sketch map of sites in the Gort lowlands (Excursion G). The dashed blue lines are only to indicate proven connections between sinks and risings. The actual drainage routes undoubtedly are far more complex.*

Excursion A: The Coast and Corkscrew Hill.

This excursion follows one of the most popular tourist trails, a route taken by many of the Burren coach tours operating out of Lisdoonvarna or Galway. Descending from the shale cap around Lisdoonvarna it passes through a heavily glaciated area of limestone before following the coast road northwards, around Black Head to Ballyvaghan. From there the route heads south, up the broad Ballyvaghan valley before ascending the spectacular hairpin bends of Corkscrew Hill and thence onto the shale cap once again. Some of the sites can be viewed in passing or justify only short stops, but more time can be spent at Poulsallagh, Fanore and Murroogh where there is a range of features to see.

The overall excursion is described in a clockwise direction from Lisdoonvarna since this affords better views of some of the large-scale features. It makes an excellent cycle ride with only one major climb, at Corkscrew Hill, though there are several long gradual inclines en route.

A1. Lisdoonvarna to the shale margin

For about the first 4 km west of Lisdoonvarna the road is across the undulating outcrop of Clare Shales which lie above the limestone along the southern edge of the Burren. The shales form a rather bleak landscape of damp acidic soils with abundant sedge, very different from the well-drained soils and famous flora found on the limestones.

A2. Craggycorradan (R 103997)

Stopping, with care, by the roadside at this sharp right-hand bend affords spectacular views across the landscape. Directly to the north the tower of Ballynalackan Castle overlooks the normally dry gorge of the lower Coolagh River. Further sections of this gorge can be seen to the west and north-west **(Stop E5)** before it peters out in a broad flat area, criss-crossed by stone walls, as the coast is approached. This dry valley may have been formed during glacial periods when permafrost, blocking the undergound drainage, forced meltwater to flow on the surface and carve out this impressive gorge. Even today extreme floods cause the Coolagh River sink **(Stop F1)**, 1.5 km to the north-east, to overflow. A continuous surface river may then flow past the castle and has been known to flood the road here.

P - there is only very limited space for parking at the roadside here.

A3. Oughtdarra

Descending from the Ballynalackan cross-roads there are fine views of the rounded shale summit of Knockauns to the north-east and the glacially plucked crags and terraces of Oughtdarra below. Continuing on, the road winds through chaotic heaps of glacial debris scattered with massive limestone erratics left by the retreating ice sheets, and now thickly clothed with thorn and hazel scrub.

A4. Poulsallagh (M 085017)

It is worth stopping to look around this small but fascinating bay. Features on the south side of the bay are described for **Stop D13**. To the north of the bay an extensive area of

Figure 18. *Kamenitzas, or solution pans, enclosed by irregular raised rims, on limestone pavement north of Poulsallagh (Stop A4).*

limestone pavement has limestone erratics scattered across its surface, some perched on conspicuous pedestals left as the limestone surface around has been lowered by dissolution **(see Figure 9)**. Shallow solution pans, or **kamenitzas**, are common on smoother areas of the pavement. Intriguingly, many have irregular rims rising a cm or more above the surrounding limestone **(see Figure 18)**. Water, containing limestone dissolved from the kamenitza, splashes on to the surrounding surface in windy weather and then evaporates to leave a thin calcite film. Falling rain must then dissolve this calcite film before it can attack the limestone beneath. As a result the surface of the 'splash zone' is lowered more slowly than the surrounding limestone, forming these rims.

There are two interesting sections of cave passage at Poulsallagh. Poulsallagh cave itself pierces the crag immediately north of the boulder beach. It has been followed northwards for several tens of metres, meandering past two roof openings, to a boulder blockage. The passage has the tall narrow appearance of a vadose canyon, but undulating notches and ledges on the walls **(see Figure 19)**, visible even in the unroofed seaward end of the passage, show that it actually formed *below* the water table by paragenesis. Just inside the entrance of Poulsallagh cave the passage walls are dissected by small pinnacles and ridges, up to a few centimetres long, which are orientated towards the light. These are **photokarren**, which form by the etching action of blue-green algae which live just below the surface of the rock. About 100 metres to the north-east a largely unroofed cave passage cuts inland from the cliff. Where the roof survives at thc landward end some of the original sediments still survive. They are remarkable for the abundance of quartz pebbles they contain (quartz is a very rare mineral on the Burren, though common in many other places), together with pebbles of Galway granite and Connemara schists. These rock types show that the material came from the north side of Galway Bay. Ice must have carried

Figure 19. *Paragenetic canyon in Poulsallagh Cave (Stop A4). The undulating ledges on the walls are typical of this type of cave and mark the former position of successive sediment levels (sediment since eroded out). They distinguish it from a vadose canyon, where similar ledges always slope downstream or are nearly horizontal. Note the conspicuous scalloping of the walls, which indicates the direction and speed of water flow (see Figure 15).*

them here, later to be swept into the cave by streams eroding the boulder clay. Granite and quartz are rare in boulder clay found on the surface of the Burren today, which instead is mostly full of pieces of limestone. This suggests that these quartz-rich deposits came from an older boulder clay which was swept from the surface by the most recent glaciation.

P - there is plenty of parking on the landward side of the road just north of Poulsallagh Bay.

A5. Mirror Wall (M 089029)

Less than a kilometre further north along the road a conspicuous dry stone wall extends west from the road. From here it is a short walk to the edge of Mirror Wall, though **take care since the cliff falls sheer into the sea**. Popular with climbers, this strikingly smooth cliff more than 30 metres high has developed as cliff falls have exposed a major north-south joint surface.

P - there is space for parking just to the south of the drystone wall on the landward side of the road.

A6. Fanore beach (M 137082)

Walk west from the car park to the broad sandy beach fronting the dune system. Where the Caher River enters the sea the pebbles at its mouth are coated with a creamy-white crust of calcite deposited by the river, which further upstream flows across boulder clay full of ground-up limestone rich in calcium carbonate. In places the dunes, and sometimes the beach sand, have been stripped back to reveal an ancient limestone pavement, with the grikes often filled with cemented sands. Further north along the beach the south-facing

flanks of limestone ledges and boulders have been facetted and polished by sand blown against them by the prevailing south-westerly winds.
P - there is an obvious car park on the landward side of the dunes.

A7. Murroogh (M 146107)

Between the road and the shore an extensive area of limestone pavement terraces shows fine examples of clints, grikes, kamenitzas and other features, and supports a profusion of typical Burren plants. To the south a grassy ridge of boulder clay, deposited in the lee of the hill to the north-east, rises from the pavement. Scattered granite boulders are further evidence of ice movement across Galway Bay. Near the road are some particularly fine examples of limestone erratic boulders perched on pedestals which, acting like umbrellas, have protected the limestone beneath from dissolution **(see Figure 9)**. However, this site is a stark example of the thoughtless destruction caused by some tourists, with rock slabs ripped up to construct miniature 'dolmens' and boulders toppled from their pedestals.
P - there is space for a few cars by the roadside on the bend north of Murroogh.

A8. Black Head (M 154122)

Black Head probably takes its name from the dark colour of the weathered dolomite here, with a thick bed of this rock exposed on the lower slopes. Several small caves in the cliff opposite the lighthouse appear to be relicts of ancient phreatic passsages long since truncated by glacial and marine erosion. East of Black Head the northward-facing scarp, smoothed and rounded by the southward movement of ice more than 14,000 years ago, plunges steeply to the sea from a height of more than 250 metres **(see Figure 20)**.
P - there is only very limited parking space near Black Head lighthouse.

A9. Pinnacle Well, Tobercornan (M 201097)

A small, gothic-style shelter has been built over the limestone pavement where water emerges from a small spring. The output from this spring changes little throughout the year, even after heavy rain, indicating that the water comes from slow and diffuse percolation through the limestone rather than from a discrete stream sink.
P - there is ample parking on either side of the holy well.

A10. Corkscrew Hill (M 206027)

The viewpoint near the top of Corkscrew Hill affords spectacular views northwards along the Ballyvaghan valley and adjacent hills. The hills east of the valley are entirely of limestone, as are most of those to the west. Immediately west of the viewpoint Poulacapple still retains a sedge-covered shale cap. The Ballyvaghan Valley, and the Turlough Valley to the east, are very old features of the Burren. They were formed originally by streams draining northwards when the shale cap extended much further across the Burren and the Gort lowlands extended out into what is now Galway Bay.
P - there is ample parking at the viewpoint.

Figure 20. The glacially rounded northern scarp of the Burren, near Black Head (Stop A8), descending steeply to the sea.

A11. Doonyvardan (M 198019)

Extending south from Corkscrew Hill is a vast plateau of limestone pavement, often obscured by hazel and thorn scrub. Just beyond the minor road south to Kilfenora, at Doonyvardan, there is an abrupt steepening of the slope and change in vegetation to sedge and conifer plantations. This marks the boundary between the limestone and the overlying Clare Shales of Poulacapple.

A12. Eastern Slieve Elva

Emerging from the conifers on Poulacapple the road descends gently onto the limestone again with patches of limestone pavement interspersed with grassed over boulder clay. Across the valley to the north-west lies the steep eastern scarp of Slieve Elva, beneath which lies the Poulnagollum cave system, the longest in Ireland with more than 14 km of explored passages **(see Excursion F)**.

A13. Lisdoonvarna

Continuing the gentle descent into Lisdoonvarna the road passes back onto the shale outcrop, giving way to a landscape of rounded, sedge-covered drumlins. The small town of Lisdoonvarna became a spa town in 1845 following the discovery of several small springs, each with a distinct chemistry supposed to confer medicinal properties. Of these, the Iron Well, Magnesia Well and Sulphur Well are still exploited on a small scale and the opportunity to taste them should not be missed. All of these springs emerge from the Clare Shales above the limestone. Although the shale supposedly is an impermeable rock, numerous fractures within it allow enough groundwater movement to feed these springs. Decomposition of iron pyrite (iron sulphide) and other minerals within the shales produce the distinctive chemistry, and taste, of the water.

P - there is ample parking in the town.

Excursion B: Aillwee and Poulnabrone

This excursion **(Excursion Map 1)** makes an interesting alternative to **stops A10-A12 of Excursion A**. About 1.5 km south-west of Ballyvaghan the road for Kilfenora and Aillwee Cave bears off to the left. Other than the minor road which leads up to Aillwee cave itself, the same road is followed to Sheshymore, then turn east to Carran where it intercepts the route of **Excursion C**.

B1. Aillwee Cave (M 233048)

This site, the only cave in the Burren easily accessible to the general public, is well worth a visit and remains one of the most enigmatic karst features of the area. The most striking feature throughout much of the cave is the superb phreatic half-tube in the roof. This lies at about the level of the clay band forming the lowest of the nine terraces in the Burren and cave formation probably was influenced by the clay's impermeable nature. The passage shape shows that the cave formed originally beneath the local water table yet it now lies more than 90 metres above the floor of the Ballyvaghan valley below, suggesting that it formed when the landscape was very different from today. The half-tube is less than a metre across near the entrance but more than 2 metres across in the roof of The Highway, at the current limit of the show cave. In places the bedding plane immediately below the half-tube shows a network of much smaller intertwining half-tubes, known as **anastomoses**. The main tube probably developed through preferential enlargement of one of these 'proto caves'. When originally discovered the entrance passage was almost full to the roof with sediment; this level is clearly visible as a distinct line along the walls at about head-height. Further into the cave percolating water has washed away much of this sediment in places to reveal a deep canyon passage. This canyon lies below the bedding plane on which the half-tube and small 'proto-caves' initially formed, and so it must have been produced by a stream cutting down into the floor once the local water table had fallen below the level of the half-tube. As such it is a good example of a vadose canyon **(see figures 13 and 14)**. Near the end of the show cave water cascades down into the passage from a vadose shaft in the roof. Elsewhere, stalactites and stalagmites have formed where water, percolating down fractures in the limestone, has redeposited calcite. Dating of these shows that the vadose canyon had already formed more than half a million years ago.

The active stream beyond the show cave flows outwards and, in flood, may inundate the whole cave. Dye tests show that the water leaving Aillwee Cave reappears in Ballyvaghan Bay, but the source of the water entering the cave remains a mystery.

The exit tunnel, although artificial, intercepted several sections of natural cave passage during its construction and these can still be seen.

P - there is ample parking at this major visitor attraction.

B2. Gragan East (M 223036)

Rejoining the main route the road south ascends, from the rich pasture on the boulder clay covering the floor and lower slopes of the Ballyvaghan Valley, onto an extensive area of gently sloping limestone pavement overlooking the head of the valley.

P - there is rough parking by the roadside here.

B3. Glensleade (M 230012)

The road passes southwards onto a deeply dissected area of limestone which contrasts with the smoother surface to the north. To the west of the road is an irregular closed depression, or uvala, up to 30 metres deep and covering more than 1.5 km^2. South from here are many small closed depressions to the east of the road and, visible in the crags beyond, are several small gorges extending to the north-east. All of these point to a long history of karstification in this part of the Burren.

B4. Poulnabrone Dolmen (M 236004)

This is one of the most visited sites on the Burren yet the fine karst features visible around, and even on, this archaeological monument are overlooked by most visitors. Immediately east of the road is a large, sub circular, rock-walled doline about 10 metres deep **(see Figure 8)**, with other, shallower, grass-floored, dolines on either side of the road nearby. The immediate area of the dolmen is of typical limestone pavement with very prominent north-south jointing. The sill-stone at the entrance to the dolmen chamber was placed in an east-west grike and hence the dolmen itself is orientated roughly parallel to the main joint set. Some of the major joints now form grass-floored avenues between areas of pavement while a larger and deeper gully east of the dolmen extends north and divides into two still larger gullies which continue to the north and north-east. The dolmen's capstone slopes to the south yet the small solution pans, or kamenitzas, on top have horizontal floors showing that they have formed since the dolmen was constructed about 5,800 years ago **(see Figure 21)**.

P - park by the roadside here.

Figure 21. *Kamenitzas (solution pans) on the capstone of Poulnabrone Dolmen (Stop B4). Although the capstone is tilted, the kamenitza floors are horizontal. This demonstrates that they have formed, or at least been substantially modified, since the dolmen was built.*

B5. Carran Church (R 240974)

This 15th Century church and graveyard overlook the vast closed depression, up to 70 metres deep, extending 2 km north-east to Meggagh **(see Stop C11)**. Its rocky slopes and cliffs are, in places, buried beneath grassed-over boulder clay, proving that the depression is older than the last

Figure 22. Lough Aleenaun (Stop B6) in dry weather, viewed from the south. In flood the entire basin in front of the crag fills up, fed by springs rising in the woodland behind. The water drains away again mainly via sinks below the left hand side of the crag.

glaciation. Flood water draining from Meggagh may reappear at Lough Aleenaun **(Stop B6)** en route to the Fergus River **(Stop C3)**.
P - park close to the side of the road.

B6. Lough Aleenaun (R 249954)

Near the south-western end of the minor road to Carran there are fine views southwards to the closed depression which (sometimes) contains Lough Aleenaun. A low drumlin on the south side of the depression has impounded the lake, which is fed by springs emerging on its north side and drains via several sinks at the lake margins. In wet weather it can fill to a depth of 3-4 metres in only a few hours, but it may drain completely after little more than a week of dry weather **(see Figure 22)**.

B7. large doline (R 253963)

A kilometre east of the road junction a large doline **(see Figure 8)** lies to the north of the road. This one has cliffed walls up to 10 metres high and an undulating grassy floor, probably underlain by boulder clay left by the last glaciation. It might seem odd that glaciation did not destroy dolines like this or fill them completely with boulder clay. They may have been occupied by stagnant ice over which the main ice sheets moved, thereby minimising any erosion or infilling.

North-east from here the route intercepts **Excursion C** at Carran **(Stop C10)**.

Excursion C: Kilfenora-Corofin-Carran Circuit

This tour **(Excursion Map 1)** passes through some of the large scale karst landforms which are characteristic of the south-east part of the Burren. Among the most conspicuous are large closed depressions, or **uvalas**, lacking any surface inlet or outlet, which represent a diagnostic feature of karst landscapes. They may originally have developed as '**karst windows**' where holes, or 'windows', eroded through a former shale cover concentrated drainage onto the underlying limestone. Some of the best examples in the Burren are visited on this excursion. The route is best followed by bike or small car, since it follows fairly narrow roads with limited parking at most places. It is worth taking time to visit the Burren Centre in Kilfenora before you set out or on your return.

C1. East of Kilfenora

The road for 4 to 5 km east of Kilfenora mostly lies on the top of the limestone and just north of the shale edge. Classic 'basket-of-eggs' **drumlin** topography is a very obvious feature of the land south of the road. These drumlins were formed by glacial moulding of the boulder clay as the ice sheet 'decayed' towards the end of the last glaciation.

C2. Ballyclancahill sink (R 218933)

An artificially straightened stream has incised itself into the eastern end of a long flat field, crossed by wooden pylons, to sink just south of the road. Conspicuous collapse hollows in the soil nearby act as flood overflow sinks but after heavy rain a temporary lake may form. Centuries of accumulated lake sediment have formed the flat floor of the field.

C3. Fergus River (R 253925)

This spot affords fine views of some major features of the south-east Burren. The conifer-clad slopes rising on the south side of the valley mark the northern edge of the shale and the southern limit of the Burren. The stepped scarp of Clifden Hill, to the south-east, represents the southern extremity of the Burren's abrupt eastern scarp. The Fergus River meanders eastwards across the broad, limestone-floored, valley below en route to Lough Inchiquin. The river is fed by three groups of springs; Fergus Risings almost directly below this viewpoint, Poulnaboe about 1 km upstream, and Elmvale Risings about 1 km downstream. Together they drain almost 40% of the Burren. Only Elmvale Risings flow throughout the year but following heavy rain a conspicuous river may pour from the Fergus Risings, hidden in scrub at the foot of the slope here, to join the main river a few hundred metres south. The Fergus River valley is a very ancient feature of the Burren. Stalagmites from Fergus River Cave, at the head of the Fergus Risings, have been dated to more than 350,000 years old.

P - there is limited parking either side of the road.

C4. Killinaboy 'mushroom stones' (R 273915)

Where the Kilfenora-Corofin road crosses a minor tributary to the Fergus River, several peculiar undercut rocks can be seen in a field immediately to the north. These are 'mushroom stones' or 'wave stones'. They formed when the level of Lough Inchiquin

Figure 23. *'Mushroom Stone', or 'Wave Stone', one of several at Killinaboy (Stop C4). The conspicuous notch about halfway up indicates the former water level of Lough Inchiquin prior to draining.*

was higher and lapped against these limestone boulders, etching away at the submerged parts. Drainage works in the 19th Century lowered the level of the lake and the shoreline now lies more than a kilometre further south across a broad flat marshy area.
NB - there is no safe parking nearby but, if you missed them on the way out, you can catch them on the way back!

C5. Lough Inchiquin (R 275894)

A minor road leading to the lake crosses a rounded 20 metre high grassy ridge of boulder clay, left by the last ice sheet, before descending to the shore. The lake lies on the western edge of the limestone lowlands, barely 20 metres above sea level. Immediately to the west the steep scarp of Clifden Hill looms more than 150 metres higher. Protected from rainwater dissolution by a thick cover of shale, the top of the limestone on Clifden Hill lies more than 50 metres above the adjacent lowlands. Several limestone knolls nearby probably represent hills stripped of their shale cover comparatively recently and so exposed to dissolution for perhaps 100,000 years or less. By contrast, the limestone forming the lowlands has probably been exposed to dissolution for a million years or more.
P - there is ample parking at the lake shore.

C6. Parknabinnia (R 265935)

East of the road, virtually opposite Parknabinnia wedge tomb, a huge limestone boulder rests on a conspicuous pedestal rising 40 cm above the surrounding limestone pavement. In the same way as the shale cap of Clifden Hill, visible to the south, has protected the limestone beneath from dissolution, so this boulder has protected the limestone which now forms the pedestal. Its height is a measure of how much the surrounding limestone has been lowered by dissolution. Areas of limestone pavement nearby dip gently to the west and are furrowed by solution runnels.
P - there is parking on the roadside verge. Cross the wall using the stone stile near the more southerly of two rusty posts.

C7. Commons North (R 267944)

Grassy limestone pavement, dipping gently west, extends across much of the open land west of the road. There are fine solution runnels in places and many other features typical of limestone pavement. Several large linear depressions cross the area from east to west. Their origin is unclear but they probably correspond to zones of more closely spaced fractures where dissolution has been enhanced by better drainage.

P - there is ample parking on the roadside here.

C8. Cahercommaun (R 282965)

From the road a fairly easy path meanders through limestone pavement overgrown with hazel scrub, crossing a deep depression before climbing steeply on to an extensive level area of grassy limestone pavement. The 1200 year old stone fort of Cahercommaun lies on the edge of this pavement, overlooking an impressive gorge. A grass-topped 'island' separates this gorge from the deeper scrub-filled channel of Glencurran beyond. To the north-east this channel seems to fade out on the slopes east of the Carran depression. To the south-west it is joined by a 'tributary' channel - the grassy depression crossed en route to the fort - and continues south-west for a kilometre or more. Gorges like this are a conspicuous feature of the Burren but their origin is, in many cases, unclear. At least some were probably eroded by glacial summer meltwater flowing across the surface during a cold period of the Ice Age, when underground drainage channels were frozen solid.

P - park at the start of the track, at R 274960.

C9. Glencurran (R 275965)

North from the Cahercommaun car park the road descends into the scrub-choked gorge of Glencurran before climbing onto a broad grassy expanse of boulder clay which separates Glencurran from the Carran depression to the north.

C10. Carran Depression (R 285985)

With an area of more than 7 km^2 this is the largest closed depression on the Burren. The sides of the depression, in places draped with grass-covered patches of boulder clay, rise steeply for several tens of metres above it. The floor of much of the depression is strikingly flat with the Castletown River flowing sluggishly across it. Deposits of boulder clay and lake sediment, together with chert layers in the limestone beneath, keep the river on the surface. Water sinks at the southern end of the depression to re-emerge from springs on the Fergus River more than 6 km to the south. In wet weather these mud-choked sinks are unable to take all of the flow and the depression floods, often for several months.

P - there is ample parking around the village.

C11. Meggagh (R 255987)

The road heading east from Carran climbs steeply to a plateau of grassy limestone pavement before plunging spectacularly some 70 metres into the Meggagh depression. This is a classic closed depression, the diagnostic landform of karst landscapes. In wet weather a temporary lake forms in the lowest part, fed by numerous springs and draining,

Figure 24. *Looking north across the uvala at Kilcorney (Stop C12). The sinuous drainage channel ends just short of the entrance to the Cave of the Wild Horses, which lies at the foot of the cliffs in the right foreground.*

via sinks, to eventually emerge at the Fergus risings. The southern end of the Meggagh depression can be viewed from Carran Church **(Stop B5)**.

C12. Kilcorney (R 225995)

This has a more irregular shape than the Carran or Meggagh depressions, and cliffed sides in many places. It is also unusual in being associated with a large cave system. In the Cave of the Wild Horses more than 800 metres of explored passages descend 58 metres below the depression's floor. Its entrance lies at the foot of the cliff south of the ruined church, with other sections of large passage higher in the cliffs nearby. **Only experienced cavers should attempt to explore the main cave.** A sinuous channel meanders across the floor of the main depression from a boulder-filled hollow near the middle to a boulder-filled depression at the foot of the cliff just north of the cave entrance **(see Figure 24)**. After prolonged wet weather the Kilcorney depression and the cave beneath may fill rapidly from below. Noises associated with this flooding may perhaps be the source of the cave's name. The water subsequently drains back into the cave via the sinuous channel.
P - there is parking space for only one or two cars near the ruined church here.

C13. South to Kilfenora

For much of the final part of the route the road follows the limestone-shale boundary, with rush-covered shale slopes to the west and grassy limestone pavement to the east.

Excursion D: The coast from Doolin to Poulsallagh

Traversing the coast northwards from Doolin to Poulsallagh **(see Excursion Map 2, inset)** is a splendid walk in itself but also provides an opportunity to observe the 'anatomy' of the upper part of the limestone succession. Bedding planes, joints and faults are all picked out by marine weathering and erosion, while the peculiar coastal karst is spectacularly displayed at low tide. This excursion can be traversed only on foot, with the full walk (one way) taking 3-4 hours. Though the terrain is rather uneven in places, there are no major climbs to negotiate. **Great care should be taken on this walk since the terrain is quite rough in places and there are certain sections where the cliffs fall sheer into the sea. It is inadvisable to attempt the walk during stormy weather**.

P - there is ample parking at either end of the walk, at Doolin Quay and at Poulsallagh (see stop A4).

D1. Doolin Strand (R 065963)

Fisherstreet Bay forms the extreme south-west corner of the Burren. The top beds of the Carboniferous Limestone, seen on the north side of the bay, dip gently southwards below the Clare Shales which form the dark cliffs stretching south-westwards to the Cliffs of Moher and beyond. The Aille River reaches the sea near the centre of the bay only in flood. Normally it sinks into its bed further upstream **(see Stop E1)** and enters the Doolin River Cave. Water from the cave may well up through the sand near the mouth of the Aille River, or from bedding planes in the limestone just to the north, but most emerges from the sea bed about 100 metres offshore.

D2. Doolin Point and Hell (R 056974)

Near the seaward end of Doolin Point lies a spectacular, partly unroofed, vadose cave passage, known locally as 'Hell'. Developed on a major north-south joint, it descends below sea level to the north and must have formed when sea level was lower. Remnants of four small phreatic tubes emerge from the bedding plane at the foot of the crag to the east and meander towards Hell. **Only experienced cavers or climbers should attempt to descend into Hell, and even then only at low tide and in calm weather**. Ledges exposed at low tide on the south side of Doolin Point, and all along this stretch of coast, have been etched by various, often microscopic, marine organisms into a fantastic array of irregular pinnacles and pools encrusted with barnacles and mussels. The floors of the largest, and lowest, of these pools are studded with spiny sea urchins (*Paracentrotus lividus*), each of which occupies its own made-to-measure hollow **(see Figure 10)**.

D3. Boodaun (R 057976)

In this small bay, just north of Doolin Point, the vertical joints and horizontal bedding planes of the limestone are very clearly displayed **(see Figure 5)**. The strikingly stepped form of the coast here also demonstrates how the Burren coast is being eroded by the sea. Blocks plucked by the waves are thrown inland to form the spectacular storm beach behind, testifying to the awesome power of some of the storms which strike this Atlantic

Figure 25. *A 'boil' of fresh water rising to the surface from the drowned Mermaid's Hole cave system, 10 metres beneath Boodaun (Stop D3).*

coast. Boulder clay with striated boulders rests on glacially striated limestone in places immediately behind this storm beach.

A major cave passage, Mermaid's Hole, emerges some 10 metres below sea level at Boodaun and is associated with several blow holes on the platform above. Occasionally, in calm weather following heavy rain, fresh water can be seen rising to the surface of Boodaun from this cave **(see Figure 25)**. Mermaid's Hole has been followed inland for almost a kilometre and is just part of a whole complex of drowned cave passages which lie beneath Doolin Point and Boodaun, of which only Hell is accessible to non-divers.

Continue northwards across southward-dipping ledges backed by a storm-beach of massive boulders. The limestone here, and for some distance north, contains many irregular bands and nodules of **chert**. Being insoluble, these weather out as knobbly black layers **(see inside front cover)**.

D4. Poulcraveen (R 064981)

Approaching Poulcraveen Bay from the south, the storm beach of large angular limestone blocks plucked from the cliffs gives way towards the back of the bay to more rounded boulders which have come from erosion of the adjacent boulder clay. Although most are of limestone, there are also boulders of pale brown sandstone and occasional black limestone nodules packed with spirally-coiled shells of fossil goniatites, a distant, and long extinct, relative of the squid. Both are from the Clare Shales and show that the ice travelled across the shale to reach this point.

Figure 26. *Looking out from the paragenetic canyon at Poulcraveen (Stop D4), a 'pre-glacial' passage which has been truncated by glacial and marine erosion.*

The bay is backed by a limestone cliff, in places buried beneath boulder clay. Just north of the main cliff the limestone shows striking glacial striations with a north-east to south-west orientation **(see Figure 6)**. Several short sections of cave passage pass through this cliff and obviously have been truncated by glacial erosion. Hence they must be older than the last ice advance. With care, the largest **(see Figure 26)** can be traversed at low tide **although the boulders here are very slippery**. The shape of these passages is rather like typical vadose canyons, formed above the water table, but several clues show that they are actually paragenetic canyons formed below the water table **(see Figures 12, 13 and 14)**. Firstly, small tributary passages actually join the main passage quite low on the wall. They show that the roof level rose after the passages first formed. Secondly, towards the northern end of the cliff there is a prominent arch, a remnant of cave roof, which lies about two metres above a bedding plane with many small tubes or 'proto caves'. This too shows that the roof level rose after the cave first formed. In a vadose canyon the 'proto caves' and the roof of each tributary passage would be at the same level as the roof of the main passage, with the 'canyon' cutting down into the limestone beneath.

D5. The Trug (R 066986)

Continuing northwards a series of broad stepped coastal platforms rise gently with the dip of the limestone over a distance of several hundred metres. Where the coast swings eastwards, towards a sheer, north-south, joint-aligned cliff plunging 30 metres to the sea, the limestone platform is breached by The Trug. This spectacular deep and narrow gully extends almost 100 metres south from the cliff edge and has developed along a minor **fault** where the limestone on the west side has been downthrown by about 1.5 metres. This fault can be traced, sometimes forming a prominent step, in other places a boulder-choked gully, for several hundred metres further south to where it becomes buried beneath the storm beach. At the foot of the terrace immediately landward of this small fault scarp a prominent bedding plane is riddled with innumerable small anastamosing tubes ('proto-caves') and a few larger phreatic half tubes up to a metre or so across. The larger tubes have large scallops indicating rather slow water flow down-dip to the south. Like the passages at Poulcraveen, with which these tubes may once have been linked, they formed when the water table was higher and the coast lay much further west.

D6. North from The Trug

At the southern end of The Trug ascend eastwards to the next main terrace, which is backed by a storm beach of plucked limestone blocks and more rounded cobbles reworked from the boulder clay. Immediately behind is a two metre high face of orange-brown boulder clay, with rounded cobbles of limestone and a few of sandstone, resting on a strikingly smooth limestone surface with clear NNE-SSW glacial striations. These striations have been erased by recent dissolution only a short distance in front of the present limit of the boulder clay.

D7. Lackglass (R 072995)

At the northern end of the sheer cliff described at **Stop D5**, a stepped descent can be made to reach intertidal ledges at Lackglass. The cliff here swings inland into a shallow gully, eroded along a WSW-ENE fracture, with the shore below strewn with house-sized boulders plucked from the cliff. Their huge size reflects the presence of a particularly massive bed of limestone, almost 10 metres thick, in the lower part of the cliff. A metre-thick limestone bed above this is particularly rich in fossil brachiopod shells **(see Figure 4)**. Below this massive bed the ledge is scarred with parallel grooves and ridges orientated almost north-south **(see Figure 27)**. They can be traced across this entire bedding plane for several hundred metres northwards, and more can be seen on the next major bedding plane 10 metres higher. These striations can be traced into the cliff and clearly are different from the glacial striations seen on many rock surfaces elsewhere. They are called **slickensides** and formed when rock scraped past rock during earthquakes. They show that ancient earth movements caused some of the limestone beds in the Burren to slide across each other.

Several small caves can be seen at this locality. Sharp-eyed visitors might spot a small vadose canyon, choked with brown pebbly mud and sand, meandering tightly through the shattered limestone bedrock among the boulder chaos in the centre of the bay. At low tide the intertidal ledge can be followed southwards, down-dip around the headland into two other fracture-guided gullies. The headland itself is pierced by a network of small phreatic tubes which have developed along the slickensided fault plane. **It should be remembered that these small and constricted passages are completely flooded by the incoming tide**. The slickensided ledge can be followed up-dip to the north, becoming narrower as a white-dappled crag, formed on a joint-aligned calcite vein, is approached. Two phreatic half-tubes in this crag are developed on the slickensided bedding plane. One can be followed (crawling only!) for some 40 metres

Figure 27. *Slickensides, grooves and ridges formed when two masses of rock slide past each other during an ancient earthquake, on a bedding plane at Lackglass (Stop D7). A small elliptical phreatic tube has formed later, meandering across the faulted bedding plane.*

north-eastwards to a blockage of boulders and sand washed in from a surface collapse.

Retrace your steps southwards to the shallow gully before ascending to the top of the cliff and continuing northwards once more. This passes over a massive sea cave at the back of a shallow bay. A shallow boulder-choked depression in the fretted limestone pavement just inland from the southern corner of this bay marks the point of collapse into the small cave passage mentioned in the previous paragraph. A little further north the joints several metres inland from the cliff edge have started to gape as the sea cave beneath undermines the cliff; not a place for the faint-hearted.

D8. North from Lackglass

Just north of the sea cave there is an easy descent back onto the slickensided bedding plane. Negotiating a small area of giant boulders strewn across the cliff top, descend at any convenient and safe spot on to the next major terrace below to examine a small crag just south of another 'tongue' of monumental boulders extending across the terrace. The lowest half metre of this crag is formed of very rubbly limestone resting on a pitted surface with deep hollows. These features represent a palaeokarst surface, the ancient equivalent of a limestone pavement but formed during the early Carboniferous, about 340 million years ago, when sea level dropped briefly to expose the limestone to weathering. Just north of this 'tongue' of boulders an obvious phreatic cave passage, about a metre

Figure 28. Drained phreatic half-tube, north of Lackglass (Stop D8). This has developed above a much older limestone pavement, or palaeokarst surface, pitted with hollows. One of these hollows, filled with iron-stained greenish shale, is beneath the undercut to the left of the cave entrance.

across, lies at the foot of the crag. It appears to have formed immediately above an impervious shale band associated with the ancient palaeokarst surface **(Figure 28)**. Fossil brachiopod shells are abundant on the limestone surfaces nearby.

D9. Glasha More Bay (M 077002)

Either remain on the palaeokarst surface and ascend to the north or else descend to a lower terrace and then reascend as the small cliffed bay of Glasha More is approached, skirting around it to the east. Large limestone erratic boulders, often with a yellow cap of the lichen *Xanthoria*, lie scattered across the hillside in this area, recalling the giant stone heads of Easter Island.

Glasha More is a small narrow bay developed at the foot of a dry valley. The beach is of large limestone cobbles but there are also numerous fragments of creamy flowstone and **tufa** broken off deposits left by percolation springs in the higher part of the bay. The dry valley can be followed inland between low crags, ending where it intercepts a north-south trending grassy linear depression 2 to 3 metres wide. This latter feature can be traced southwards for hundreds of metres, but follow it instead northwards, down the hill, to a narrow steep-sided inlet. This, and the linear feature just descended, have developed along a minor fault, with calcite veining clearly visible where erosion has removed the soil cover on the cliff top.

D10. North from Glasha More

Continuing northwards the cliffs become lower and the coast is dominated by massive storm beaches. Thin patches of boulder clay and smoothed, rounded areas of limestone testify to the effects of glacial erosion and deposition. A 'natural bridge' parallel to the cliff edge has formed some 800 metres north of Glasha More as marine erosion has plucked blocks from between the north-south joints in the limestone. This section of coast affords splendid views north-east to the limestone crags and terraces of Oughtdarra, tailing off towards the coast, and the shale cap of Knockauns Mountain rising to the east.

D11. Cancapple (M 084014)

The boulder storm beach here, derived from plucking of the limestone outcrops, is backed by a lower beach of much smaller, well-rounded cobbles derived from erosion of boulder clay. These cobbles are mostly of limestone and pale brown sandstone, the latter from the Clare Shales. Occasional more exotic lithologies include pieces of Galway granite and Connemara schists which have been transported as much as 50 km south by ice more than 14,000 years ago.

D12. 'S3' Rising (M 085016)

South of Poulsallagh Bay a series of gently dipping limestone platforms rise northwards in a series of steps to a storm beach of massive limestone blocks. At low tide a tiny bay containing small boulders - the only ones found at sea level in this area - is the location of S3, the name given to the resurgence for all of the water from the Coolagh River sink **(Stop F1)** and other sinks along the western side of Knockauns Mountain. The resurgence can be difficult to spot except following heavy rain, when the small bay is filled with brown peaty water.

D13. Poulsallagh Bay (M 085017)

The last ice sheet to cross this area moved south-eastwards to produce the glacially rounded and striated rock faces on the south side of the bay and the more angular plucked crags on the north side, while at the same time leaving a chaotic mass of broken-up rock debris as the boulder-strewn landscape immediately inland. Glacial striations, with a northeast-southwest orientation, are superbly exposed on the south side of the bay beneath boulder clay composed largely of limestone fragments and finely-powdered limestone. However, the limestone below this boulder clay is cut by a half-metre wide, north-south orientated fissure filled with a different, and older, boulder clay containing numerous pieces of granite and quartz. Being lodged in this fissure it has survived the more recent glaciations which destroyed virtually all trace of this older boulder clay on the surface.

There are several interesting things to see on the north side of the bay, and these are described in **Stop A4**. They are best reached by skirting behind the massive storm beach which occupies the centre of the bay.

Excursion E: The Burren Way

The Burren Way extends from Lahinch in the south to Ballyvaghan in the north, a distance of 45 km of fairly easy walking with a few hills **(Excursion Map 2)**. Until Doolin is reached the route is entirely on the Clare Shales and sandstones above, but thereafter it lies entirely on the limestone. Although karst features can be seen in profusion along the route, those worthy of specific mention occur only sporadically, with a particular concentration on the section between Ballynalackan and the Caher Valley. Some parts of the Burren Way are along metalled roads, and hence accessible to cars and motor bikes, but the higher parts of the route are on rough tracks which can be negotiated only on foot or with a robust bicycle. The route is described from south to north.

E1. Aille River, Doolin (R 071966)

The Burren Way descends into Doolin from the steep slopes of Clare Shales and sandstones immediately to the south. The Aille River at this point flows on the very top of the limestone and in summer may be dry for a considerable stretch upstream of the bridge, with all of the water sinking to flow through the Doolin River Cave only a few metres below the surface **(see Figure 13)**.

P - there is parking alongside the road downstream of the bridge.

E2. Fisherstreet Pot (R 075967)

A rather inconspicuous clump of scrubby trees in the field immediately north-east of the Doolin Activity Lodge marks the top of a 12 metre deep pothole which drops into the lower end of the Doolin River Cave. The upper half of the shaft is in the Clare Shales but no surface stream flows into it, showing that it has formed by collapse from below rather than as a stream sink.

E3. Roadford Bridge (R 080973)

The Aille River at this point lies upstream of the sinks which drain into Doolin River Cave. Consequently the river here will be flowing even if it is dry at Doolin. A few hundred metres upstream are the remains of early 20th Century phosphate mines. A phosphate-rich layer about a metre thick between the limestone and shale was excavated from the river bed and adjacent ground here.

P - there is parking at several places within a short distance of the bridge.

E4. Aran View Swallet (R 085983) and Doolin Road Sink (R 094978)

A small stream sinks in the field just below and to the east of Aran View. This is Aran View Swallet, one of the main entry points to the 10 km long Doolin River Cave. The passage from the sink actually passes directly beneath the cemetery! A kilometre to the east is the more spectacular Doolin Road Sink **(Stop E4a)**. The Aughoonla Stream sinks into the limestone at the foot of the shale slope here and is the largest to drain entirely into the Doolin River Cave system.

E5. Craggycorradan (R 097997)

Cliffs on either side of the road mark the edges of a major dry valley which can be traced north-eastwards, past Ballynalackan Castle (see Stop A2), to the Coolagh River sink (see Stop F1). Although probably formed by surface meltwater when the underground drainage routes were blocked by permafrost, a low grassy drumlin on the floor just east of the road shows that the valley must be older than the last glaciation which left this heap of boulder clay. Beneath the south cliff on the east side of the road is Pol an Ionain, a small cave famed for its remarkable stalactite more than 6.5 metres long.

E6. Cloghaun dolines (M 110008)

About a kilometre beyond the Ballynalackan crossroads is a large grassy closed depression just east of the road and a more elongate one just to the west. They probably formed as stream sinks, since abandoned by retreat of the shale edge.

E7 (F2) Oughtdarra (M 114018)

From the road junction here there are spectacular views across the crags and terraces of Oughtdarra. Ice moving from the north-east plucked blocks from the south-facing slopes and left countless erratic boulders and heaps of boulder clay strewn across the terraces below. Several small, but interesting, caves now exposed in the crags **(see Figure 14)** clearly pre-date the last glaciation but all are notoriously difficult to find

E8. (F3) Poulnagree (M 121034)

A large concrete tank and nearby cattle trough 30 metres west of the track are useful landmarks for this pothole, which lies just to the south and is straddled by an old water pump. An easy descent in the south-west corner affords views into a steeply descending passage, aligned along a north-south joint, that leads to 2 km of vadose streamway. Poulnagree lies well away from the shale margin on the edge of a broad limestone platform overlooking a more dissected area of limestone hollows and crags to the west. It is an old sink now largely abandoned since the shale margin was eroded back to its present position by the last glaciation. Several hollows at the shale edge east of the track mark the position of the modern sinks for this cave system.

E9. (F4) Balliny Depression (M 132038)

A shallow, north-facing, embayment has been eroded into the shale edge between the northern end of Knockauns Mountain and the shale ridge of Slieve Elva to the east. To the north the limestone surface is broken by several closed depressions of which the largest is the Balliny Depression. This is a typical uvala, with an irregular shape, steep limestone walls up to 10 metres high and a gently undulating grassy floor. It is thought to be a fairly ancient feature formed where several streams draining from the surrounding shale slopes converged. Two gullies diverge from its northern end; one extends north-north-east for several hundred metres while the other, rather less distinct, extends east-north-east. A third gully extends down the hillside from the west side of the uvala and probably formed as a flood overflow. There are several minor sinks in the floor of the uvala, either adjacent

Figure 29. *Looking north-east along the north-west flank of Slieve Elva (Stop E11/F6). Shale forms the gentle slope on the right, with the terrace on the skyline representing where the shale cover was stripped by the last glaciation. The crags and hollows in the foreground represent limestone exposed by an earlier glaciation and so subject to a much longer period of weathering and karstification.*

to the shale margin or fed by water draining off patches of boulder clay. Two important caves lie beneath the Balliny Depression. Pollballiny is more than 2 km long and contains one of the largest passages in the Burren, some 3 metres wide and up to 25 metres high. The other, Poll na gCéim, is less than 900 metres long but, at 181 metres deep, is the second deepest cave in Ireland.

E10. (F5) Kilmoon-Fanore Road & North-west Slieve Elva (M 137046)

North from Balliny the Burren Way follows a minor metalled road for a short distance before bearing off to the right along a rough track on the north-west flank of Slieve Elva. A large boulder of Galway Granite, with conspicuous pink crystals of the mineral feldspar, has been built into the base of the wall only about 5 metres north of the stone way-marker near the start of this section of track. It has been carried by ice nearly 20 km from the north side of Galway Bay. Along the first stretch of track the sedge-covered shale cap of Slieve Elva can be seen on the skyline to the east. The inconspicuous entrance of Faunarooska Cave **(see Figure 16)** lies at the foot of the shale scarp and is just one of a series of small sinks to enter this cave system along the shale edge. Beyond the southernmost sink the passage swings westwards, beneath the track, and then northwards. Cavers have explored almost 1.7 km of passages in this cave.

P - there is space for parking several cars on the metalled stretch of road.

E11. (F6) Tobar an Athar Calbach holy well (M 151053)

The track rises gently, passing a ruined stone cottage before a fainter track bears off to the east. Follow this, past a very uneven landscape of limestone crags and hollows just to the south, to reach a strikingly flat limestone platform extending out from the foot of the shale slope. A small cross marks the site of the Holy Well, which is actually a short unroofed section of minor vadose stream cave. It is fed by a stream sinking 50 metres to the east in a small hollow marked by a Goat Willow bush. A little west of the Holy Well a small scar exposes the dark grey Clare Shales above the limestone. Just beyond is another stream sink, a scrub-filled hollow from which the sound of falling water emanates. Not far to the south-west the flat limestone terrace extending from the foot of the shale slope ends abruptly at the edge of a crag overlooking a much more irregular landscape of crags, gullies and closed depressions **(see Figure 29)**. This flat platform represents limestone that was covered by shale until the last glaciation, and hence has been modified by only about 14,000 years of karstification. The more dissected landscape further out had its shale cover stripped some time earlier, perhaps in the previous glaciation, and so has experienced a much longer period of karstification. The floor of the large irregular closed depression at the southern end of this area is pocked with smaller depressions; one on the west side is a 26 metre deep vadose shaft in which falling water can be heard. Great swathes of Mountain Aven (*Dryas octopetalla*), a Burren flora speciality, are found in this area.

Continue westwards to rejoin the Burren Way. Alternatively, follow the gully north to rejoin the track heading east. This forms part of the Slieve Elva Circuit **(Excursion F)** and skirts around the shale edge, past many small sedge-covered hollows, before swinging south-east along the eastern flank of Slieve Elva.

E12. Ballyelly (M 150056)

Looking back southwards from a few hundred metres north of the fork affords a fine view of the sedge-covered shale slopes and the abrupt change from the level platform at its foot to the more dissected limestone surface further out. The track continues north-eastwards across an extensive, rather featureless, area of limestone pavement. Passing the crest of the hill the limestone surface becomes more dissected by small shallow closed depressions. As the track descends more steeply it affords fine views across the Caher Valley to the extensive pavements and terraces of Gleninagh Mountain and the surrounding hills, while to the south can be seen the conifer-clad shale cap of Poulacapple in the distance and the limestone terraces below extending northwards.

E13. Caher Valley (M 173068)

Descending to the valley floor the track joins a minor road which crosses over the Caher River, the largest perennial stream to flow across the limestone of the Burren. The water stays on the surface largely because much of the river bed is sealed with boulder clay, but also because of its steep descent against the southward dip of the limestone, giving the water less opportunity to percolate away along fractures. The water is saturated with calcium carbonate which is reprecipitated as a white crust on many stones on the river bed. Larger boulders are covered with the greenish-black moss *Cinclidotus fontinaloides* which thrives in limestone habitats which are intermittently flooded **(see back cover)**.

E14. Gleninagh - Poulacapple ridge (M 183071)

The Burren Way passes through a col on the long ridge extending south from Gleninagh Mountain to Poulacapple. The crest of this col is of bare or grassy limestone pavement, in places vandalised by the construction of 'mini dolmens' built by passing walkers. The walls on either side of the track here are built of angular slabs of limestone. In contrast the lower slopes, both on the east and west flanks, are draped with grass-covered boulder clay deposited by the retreating ice sheets. The dry stone walls on these lower slopes are very different here from those on top, being constructed of rounded boulders, mostly of limestone but sometimes of granite, taken from the boulder clay itself.

E15. Rathborney River (M 202050)

This is one of very few surface rivers on the limestone outcrop of the Burren, although it is a misfit stream quite out of proportion to the deep valley it now occupies between Gleninagh Mountain to the west and Cappanawalla to the east. Over much of its length the river flows over thick deposits of boulder clay which fill most of the valley to a depth of at least 30 metres. At the southern end of the valley, where the road swings around to the east, these boulder clay deposits end abruptly at a steep grassy slope. The almost sheer crag just to the east of this slope indicates the true depth of the valley. The river usually sinks in a muddy hollow a few hundred metres east of the Lisdoonvarna road and about 3 km south of Ballyvaghan. In wet weather this is unable to take all of the flow and extensive flooding may occur in the Ballyvaghan valley.

E16. Newtown Castle (M 217065)

There are few karst features of note to be seen from the Burren Way over the last few kilometres into Ballyvaghan. However, the 1.3 km long Newtown Trail provides an opportunity to explore the lower slopes of Cappanawalla, immediately to the west. Leaflets giving further details can be obtained from Newtown Castle.

P - there is ample parking for visitors to Newtown Castle, but parking space is otherwise very restricted on the narrow lanes in this area.

E17. Ballyvaghan Harbour (M 231083)

A low cliff of boulder clay lies on the east side of the harbour, below the road to the quay. It is typical of material left behind by the last glaciation, with abundant fragments of limestone, and occasional pieces of granite, 'floating' in a greyish-brown clay. Boulders of granite litter the shore below the cliff, with others built into dry stone walls around the village. They are relatively common here at the foot of the northern scarp of the Burren but are much more scarce further south.

P - there is plenty of parking in the village.

Excursion F: The Slieve Elva Circuit

The shale-capped hills of Slieve Elva and Knockauns Mountain are ringed by minor roads and tracks which are ideal for exploring the limestone landscapes on foot or by bicycle **(Excursion Map 2)**. The western side of this circuit follows the Burren Way and hence details of several sites are covered in that excursion **(Excursion E, stops E7-E11)**. The starting point for the Slieve Elva Circuit itself is Lisdoonvarna. There is only very limited parking for cars at a few points elsewhere along the route.

F1. Coolagh River sink and dry valley (M 126014)

The Coolagh River flows south-west from the shale slopes on the western flank of Slieve Elva and sinks at the bottom of a deep depression, just north of a minor road, where it has cut through to the limestone below. Sadly, the sink is becoming increasingly obscured by a conifer plantation. Although the sink appears to mark the end of the river's course (such entrenched sinks are often called '**blind valleys**'), a shallow continuation of the valley can be traced across the minor road and onwards to the south-west, where it deepens into the gorge which passes to the south of Ballynalackan Castle **(Stop A2)**. This dry valley represents the former course of the Coolagh River before it was captured underground. In extreme floods the cave passages beneath are unable to carry the full flow and water overflows to pour down this ancient river course once again.

F2-F6. (= E7-E11). Knockauns Mountain and western Slieve Elva

Turn right on joining the Burren Way and head north-east. The next five stops are described in **Excursion E, stops E7 to E11**.

F7. South-east from Tobar an Athar Calbach holy well (M 151053)

From the holy well follow the track eastwards, skirting around the shale edge past many small sedge-filled hollows, and then south-east along the eastern flank of Slieve Elva. There are numerous sinks at intervals along the shale margin on the north-eastern side of Slieve Elva. Often the only evidence of these is the sound of falling water among the bushes. All drain into the vast Poulnagollum-Poulelva cave system (>14 km long, the longest cave in Ireland) which extends south along the east flank of Slieve Elva.

F8. Poulnagollum (M 161037)

Where the rough track meets the minor road heading south, turn sharply north for a short distance. Just beyond a triangular layby a rusty metal post marks a stile over the wall. Crossing a small field brings you to the lip of Poulnagollum, from which project the branches of a large Ash tree growing on the floor of the pothole some 10 metres below. On the far side a waterfall cascades into a hole in the floor, while cave passages nearby lead further into this complex cave system. The Poulnagollum pothole formed by collapse where several passages converged and undermined the surface. **The pothole and the passages leading from it should be entered only by experienced cavers**.

P - there is limited parking near Pollnagollum pothole.

Figure 30. *The Gowlaun River (Stop F11) in flood. St Brendan's Well lies beneath the trees in the extreme lower right. The slopes are of Clare Shale but the river has cut down to flow on the top of the limestone beneath. In normal weather the river bed is dry upstream of St. Brendan's Well.*

F9. Killeany Rising and Owentoberlea River (M 164007)

This is the main rising for virtually all of the water sinking along the eastern side of Slieve Elva into the Poulnagollum cave system, and most of that sinking on the western side of Poulacapple into the Cullaun caves. In dry weather all of the water sinks again just north of the bridge but in extreme flood a surface river may flow from here all the way to St. Brendan's Well and into the Gowlaun River.

F10. Upper St. Brendan's Rising (R 153987)

150 metres north-east of the bridge is a flood rising for the Poulnagollum and Cullaun caves. Normally there is little to see from the bridge other than a dry river channel but, after heavy and prolonged rain, a surface river may flow all the way to St. Brendan's Well.

F11. St. Brendan's Well and the Gowlaun River (R 145985)

In dry weather this is the lowest rising for the water from Poulnagollum, which sinks in the Owentoberlea River, and that from the caves on the south-west side of Poulacapple. The water finally emerges at the lowest point where the limestone dips beneath the overlying shale. The rising itself cannot be seen from the road but a large stream flows under the bridge even when the river bed visible further upstream is quite dry. After prolonged or heavy rain a torrent may flow along this normally dry bed **(see Figure 30)**.

Excursion G: The Gort Lowlands

At first sight the Gort lowlands seem a monotonous expanse of grassy fields and limestone pavement, dotted with lakes and sandwiched between the Burren uplands and Galway Bay to the west, and the Slieve Aughty Mountains to the east. But a glance at the map reveals a remarkable lack of surface drainage. Only a few disjointed fragments of surface river are evident around Gort (much of the Dunkellin River, near Craughwell, is artificial) and many of the lakes have no surface inlet or outlet. In fact a huge and complex karst drainage system lies beneath the area. It goes largely unnoticed except when prolonged heavy rain overwhelms the subterranean passages and causes extensive flooding.

The Old Red Sandstone uplands of the Slieve Aughty Mountains form a major catchment from which three principal rivers drain onto the limestone. The Owenshree River in the north flows along the foot of the scarp for several kilometres to sink just north of Peterswell. To the south the Boleyneendorrish River meanders a short distance across the limestone, changing its name numerous times before splitting to enter the aptly named 'Hammerhead Sinks' south-west of Peterswell. Still further south the Owendalulleegh River flows through Lough Cutra, changing its name to the Beagh River before sinking near the Punch Bowl. The river is seen again at the surface at various points between here and Coole Lough, changing its name several more times en route. Other than in exceptional floods, water does not flow on the surface any further west of here.

The sites covered by this excursion **(Excursion Map 3)** are scattered across a large area. Hence it is necessary to cycle or drive if all are to be visited in the same day.

G1. Abbey Hill and the Corker Pass (M 313103)

Abbey Hill, in the north-east corner of the Burren, affords fine views across the Gort lowlands. In the foreground the fretted south-eastern shore of Galway Bay is formed of low hills and ridges of boulder clay separated by long inlets. Large springs emerging at the inner ends of these inlets, most notably at Kinvarra **(Stop G14)**, are the final destination of all of the water emerging from beneath the lowlands and from the northern part of the Burren. In clear weather the sandstone ridge of the Slieve Aughty mountains can be seen some 20 km to the east, rising above the remarkably flat limestone plain of the Gort lowlands.

P - park by the green road at the crest of the hill or by the bend a little lower.

G2. Cappacasheen (M 3804)

The vast expanse of low-lying, seemingly featureless, limestone pavement on either side of the road here contrasts strikingly with the eastern scarp of the Burren rising steeply just a short distance to the west. As such it is a fine example of a corrosion plain, formed by several million years of dissolutional lowering of the exposed limestone.

G3. Lough Bunny (R 380968)

Lough Bunny is a permanent lake but has no surface inlets or outlets. It is fed by numerous small springs which, in wet weather, emerge from fissures and U-shaped channels along the east shore, and drains via sinks at its northern end en route towards

Figure 31. *Gently dipping limestone on the east shore of Lough Bunny (Stop G3). Small circular solution pits, typical of limestone lake margins, cover the upper shore which is flooded only in winter. The lower shore, exposed only in summer, is covered by a chalky 'marl' crust deposited by the carbonate-saturated lake water. This marl crust protects the limestone beneath from weathering and so the lower shore remains smooth and unpitted. The eastern scarp of the Burren is visible in the distance, rising abruptly from the Gort lowlands.*

Coole Lough. Much of the eastern shore of the lough is formed on limestone bedding planes which dip gently to the west **(see Figure 31)**. The lake water is permanently saturated with calcium carbonate and so the lower parts of the lake shore, coated with a soft deposit of chalky 'marl' precipitated from the lake water, are smooth and unweathered. Higher up the shore are peculiar circular pits that are a characteristic feature of many limestone lake shores where typical limestone pavement features are absent.

P - there is a small car park opposite the eastern end of the lough.

G4. Kilmacduagh Round Tower (M 404000)

This magnificent monastic site may seem an odd place to find karst features but, since the buildings are built largely of limestone and have been around for as much as a thousand years, they have experienced dissolution in just the same way as the limestone pavements across the region. The site is dominated by the 34 metre round tower which leans 0.6 metres out of true **(see inside back cover)**. A slight change of slope on the south flank about 20 metres up indicates that remedial measures were necessary to correct this lean which, as in its more spectacular analogue in Pisa, clearly had begun before building was complete. At the base on the north side of the tower is an intriguing notch, ~2-3 cm deep, beneath a small hole **(see Figure 32)**. This notch appears to have developed through rainwater draining down through the wall. If it formed entirely since the tower was built,

Figure 32. *Evidence for the dissolution of the monasteries. The drainage hole and dissolutional notch at the base of the north side of Kilmacduagh Round Tower (Stop G4).*

around 1000 years ago, then its depth is broadly comparable with dissolution rates estimated from pedestal heights beneath erratics on the Burren.

P - there is a car park adjacent to the site.

G5. The Punch Bowl (M 457002)

The Beagh River flows west through a steep-sided gorge cut into a thick cover of boulder clay to a major sink; it is a classic example of a **blind valley**. Just west of the main sink is the Punch Bowl, a large depression formed by collapse into the passage beneath. Continued solution of the limestone and washing away of slumped material by the underground river will eventually create an open shaft down to the river itself, such as has happened at The Churn some 600 metres further west.

P - there is a small car park in the lane near the Punch Bowl.

G6. Blackwater Sink (M 453003) and The Ladle (M 452003)

The water from the Punch Bowl flows underground a short distance to reappear at the head of another gorge, or **steephead**, cut into the boulder clay south of the lane. It sinks again by the junction of the lane with the main Ennis Road (N18). Crossing the Ennis Road, peer through the hedge on the south side of the lane about 50 metres along. If you are at the right spot you will see a large hole with standing water about 10 metres down. This is The Ladle, a collapse shaft into the underground river beneath.

P - there is a lay-by adjacent to the Blackwater sink.

G7. Cannahowna Cave [Pollduagh] (M 445003)

Cannahowna Cave, or Pollduagh, lies on the north side of the small lane west of the Ennis Road (N18). A path descends to the river and to a small jetty across the cave entrance. The river last seen east of the Ennis Road reappears here from an imposing cave passage more than 10 metres wide and 3 metres high **(Figure 33)**. The roof descends gradually, dipping below the water some 50 metres in from the entrance. Cave divers have followed the river upstream for a further 250 metres, to a depth of 30 metres. In flood the river extends the full width of the entrance, but in low water conditions the river can be crossed to reach a smaller passage which carries the main flow at such times. Its tubular shape shows that it formed under phreatic conditions, below the local water table. The course of the Owendalulleegh River westwards from the limestone margin represents an ancient karst drainage route which in places looped deep below the surface. These deep loops have

Figure 33. The imposing entrance of Cannahowna Cave, or Pollduagh (Stop G7), affords a glimpse into one of the huge underground passages that lie beneath the Gort lowlands.

survived while shallower parts of the system have been destroyed by erosion and replaced by surface rivers. However, even the surviving loops are being slowly destroyed, as shown by the collapse features of the Punch Bowl and the Ladle.

P - very limited parking at the roadside, so tuck in close to the hedge.

G8. Blackrock Turlough (M 500080)

The Owenshree River flows south-west along the foot of the Slieve Aughty Mountains to sink in a deep closed depression at Blackrock. In summer it is a grassy hollow dotted with boulders covered with the characteristic Black Turlough Moss, *Cinclidotus fontinaloides* **(see back cover)**, from which the townland probably derives its name. Following winter rains the sinks are rapidly overwhelmed to form a vast lake. In the severe floods of 1995 this reached a maximum depth of almost 14 metres at one stage, flooding the road just to the south.

G9. Polldeelin Rising (M 451057)

The combined flow from the three sinking rivers reappears at a major rising in the field immediately south of Kiltartan Church **(see Figure 34)**. It meanders northwestwards for several hundred metres, en route passing underground again for about 30 metres, before entering a major sink at the foot of a drumlin (a low rounded hill of boulder clay). It reappears less than 300 metres to the west to flow southwest into Coole Lough.

P - there is a large car park opposite the church.

Figure 34. *Polldeelin Rising (Stop G9), from which the combined flow of the Owenshree, Boleyneendorrish and Owendalulleegh rivers emerges en route to Coole Lough.*

G10. Coole Lough (M 430040)

At first sight Coole Lough appears little different from many other lakes in Ireland, but this belies its significance as the 'hub' of a vast and complex underground drainage system. Drainage from the three main rivers flowing off the Slieve Aughty Mountains to the east, and from several lakes to the south, ultimately converges on Coole Lough. The lake has no surface outlet and the water passes underground on the west side of the lake in a large, boulder-choked sink. In summer this can easily cope with the volume of water flowing into the lake and water levels may fall until only a shallow channel meanders slowly from the main perennial lake to the sink. Only the abundance of the Black Turlough Moss, *Cinclidotus fontinaloides*, covering the boulders and trunks of trees along the woodland edge overlooking the lough **(see back cover)** hint at the seasonal changes in water level. In winter, when the ground is saturated and rainfall is high, the sink is overwhelmed and the lake fills rapidly, often rising 5 metres or more. Under such conditions water flows into adjacent basins, such as Newtown Turlough to the south **(Stop G11)**, via passages only a few metres below the surface. In the greatest floods, such as that of early 1995, surface rivers may flow between adjacent turloughs. Coole Lough and the surrounding turloughs act as a vast reservoir for excess flood water. Only when the inflow rate has fallen below the capacity of the outlet passage do water levels begin to fall again.

P - there is ample car parking adjacent to the Coole Park Visitor Centre.

G11. Newtown Turlough (M 427022)

An impressive artificial causeway, 'New Line', built during the Famine, rises more than 5 metres above an area of low ground to the west of Gort and overlooks Newtown Turlough to the north. In dry summers this is a vast area of green pasture bounded by areas of slightly higher ground scattered with hawthorn bushes and patches of rough limestone pavement **(Figure 35)**. A small stream trickles sluggishly beneath the causeway and is joined by another small stream emanating from a circular pool. After heavy rainfall the view is strikingly different **(Figure 36)**. Large volumes of water pour forth from the pool and are supplemented by the greatly increased volume of the stream, fed by springs to the south. Other major springs on the north side of the turlough act as overflows from Coole Lough. Eventually the whole area may become a single vast lake **(Figure 37)** and in 1995 the causeway itself was submerged beneath more than 2 metres of floodwater!

P - there is very limited parking here - tuck in close to the wall.

G12. Garryland Nature Reserve (M 413036)

Various trails through Garryland Wood pass close to several turloughs within the Coole-Garryland turlough complex. In summer these appear as grassy glades or pastures within the woods, littered with the characteristic moss-blackened boulders, but in winter the geography of the area is completely changed as the depressions fill rapidly with water. Some of the risings can be an impressive sight in full flow following heavy rain.

P - limited parking at the entrance on the western edge of Garryland Wood.

Figure 35. *Newtown Turlough (Stop G11), viewed from 'New Line', during dry weather in Summer.*

Figure 36. *Newtown Turlough (Stop G11), filling in late Autumn after heavy rain.*

Figure 37. *Newtown Turlough (Stop G11) in Winter. In extreme floods the 'New Line' causeway here would be under more than 2 metres of water!*

G13. Caherglassaun Lough (M 415063)

Caherglassaun Lough is a permanent lake with no surface inlet or outlet but shows the same seasonal fluctuations as the turloughs. A small embayment on the south shore opposite the castle, reached via a very rough track to the north of the lough, is the main inlet rising while the main sinks are at the northern end of the lough. Various collapse features around the lough, the largest immediately north of the castle, connect with an enormous phreatic cave passage beneath. Remarkably, water levels in this lough are affected by tides, even though the risings on the coast lie some 5 km away.

G14. Kinvarra Risings (M 380105)

At the southeastern end of the long inlet of Kinvarra Bay are a series of impressive intertidal risings. The largest lie between Dunguaire Castle and the small island 200 metres to the southwest **(see Figure 38)**, reached via an obvious gap in the wall opposite the holiday cottages. In flood an obvious stream of freshwater flows out into the bay, floating on the denser seawater. At low tide it is possible to cross to the small island, where a large, partly collapsed, cave passage can be seen crossing its southern end. Other springs emerge at various points along the coast to Kinvarra, with an impressive one on the south side of the harbour. The water appearing at Kinvarra has travelled underground from the eastern side of the Gort lowlands via Coole Lough, though some may originate from the eastern flanks of the Burren. The total outflow is difficult to measure but is many hundreds, if not thousands, of litres per second even at low flow.

P - there is parking in the town and near Dunguaire Castle.

Figure 38. *Intertidal rising near Dunguaire Castle, Kinvarra (Stop G14). These springs are the final destination for most of the water draining from the Gort area.*

Further information

There are many sources of information on karst landscapes, both in the literature and on the internet. For those wishing to know more about this fascinating subject, or about the geology and landscape of the Burren and Gort region, the following may be helpful.

Karst Geomorphology. ***J.N.Jennings 1985.***
Blackwell, 283 pp. An excellent introduction to many aspects of the subject.

Karst Geomorphology and Hydrology. ***Derek Ford and Paul Williams 1989.***
Unwin Hyman, 601 pp. One of the most comprehensive books available on the subject, though rather more for the specialist.

A Dictionary of Karst and Caves. ***David Lowe and Tony Waltham 2002.***
British Cave Research Association Cave Studies Series no. 10, 40 pp. A useful guide to many technical terms. Visit **www.bcra.org.uk** for information on this and on other affordable guide books to karst regions of the UK.

Encyclopedia of Cave and Karst Science. ***John Gunn (ed.) 2004.***
Fitzroy Dearborn, London. 902 pp. A massive tome, providing a wealth of information on the subject.

Geology of Galway Bay. ***Marcus Pracht and others 2004.***
Geological Survey of Ireland (www.gsi.ie): Memoir and accompanying map for Sheet 14. Provides a wealth of information on the geology of the region.

Classic Landforms of the Burren Karst. ***David Drew 2001.***
The Geographical Association, 56 pp. A very useful guide to some of the karst features of this region. Visit **www.geography.org.uk** for information on this and on other guide books to karst and landscape regions of the UK.

Caves of County Clare and South Galway. ***Graham Mullan (ed.) 2003.***
University of Bristol Spelaeological Society (**www.ubss.org.uk**), 259 pp. The most detailed published account of the Burren karst and caves, including descriptions of the geology, hydrology and geomorphological history of the region.

www.cavingireland.org - ***The website of the Spelaeological Union of Ireland.*** SUI is the official representative body for caving in Ireland and Northern Ireland.

About the Author

I have been interested in fossils and geology from the age of six. In my mid-20s I took up caving and inevitably became interested in how caves, and the landscapes above them, are formed. Since then I have visited many caves and karst regions in Ireland, the UK and beyond, but I have a particular interest in the Burren and Gort lowlands. I have been visiting the area for more than 20 years, exploring the karst landscape and searching for new caves. Curator of Palaeontology at the Ulster Museum in Belfast since 1996, I have published articles on many different aspects of geology and natural history.

Index of Technical Terms

Only the principal page numbers where these terms are explained or referred to are given here.

anastomoses - an intertwining network of small phreatic tubes, or 'proto caves' ***(p 33)***

bedding plane - a nearly horizontal (at least in the Burren) break in a rock sequence formed by original variations in depositional conditions. ***(p 12; fig 5)***

biokarst - a general term for various pinnacles and pits formed on limestone by biological processes (bioerosion). Often well-developed in the intertidal zone. ***(p 16; fig 10)***

blind valley - a stream valley which has a blind ending, rather like a cul de sac, where the stream sinks underground. ***(pp 52 & 56)***

boulder clay - jumbled debris of clay and rock left behind by glaciers. ***(p 6; fig 6)***

brachiopod - a type of shellfish, with two unequal-sized valves. ***(p 10; fig 4)***

Carboniferous - a period of geological time during which the rocks of the Burren were deposited; from about 360-290 million years ago. ***(p 7)***

chert - an impure type of flint, an amorphous form of the mineral silica. ***(p 8 & 41; Inside Front Cover)***

clint - limestone block surrounded by solutional fissures (grikes) on limestone pavement. ***(p 14; fig 7)***

Devonian - a period of geological time during which the rocks forming much of the Slieve Aughty Mountains were deposited; about 410-360 million years ago. ***(p 10)***

doline - a surface depression entirely enclosed by higher ground; the characteristic landform of karst. On rocks other than limestone such depressions would form lakes. ***(p 14; fig 8)***

dolomite - a rock type formed of calcium and magnesium carbonates. ***(p 7)***

drumlin - a rounded hill of boulder clay moulded by the movement of ice over it. ***(p 36)***

erratic - a boulder or smaller piece of rock transported from its original location by ice movement. ***(p 15; fig 9)***

fault - a fracture along which the rocks either side have moved. ***(pp 12 & 42)***

flowstone - calcium carbonate redeposited on walls or floor by percolating water. ***(p 22; fig 16)***

glacial striae -scratches formed by the passage of ice across bare rock. ***(p 12; fig 6)***

glaciokarst - a karst landscape strongly influenced by the effects of previous glaciation. ***(pp 6 & 13)***

grike - a solutionally widened vertical fracture separating clints on a limestone pavement. ***(p 14; fig 7)***

joint - a vertical fracture in the rocks caused by earth movements, but along which there has been no movement of the rocks on either side. ***(p 12; fig 5)***

kamenitza - a solution pan or shallow pool on limestone. ***(pp 14 & 29; figs 7, 18 & 21)***

karst - the general term for landscapes formed by weathering of soluble rocks; named after a region of Slovenia. ***(p 5)***

karst window - a hole eroded through an impermeable cover rock exposing a patch of limestone beneath; effectively a window onto the underlying rock. ***(p 36)***

limestone - a rock type made largely of calcium carbonate. Unlike most rocks, it is weakly soluble in water. *(p 8)*

palaeokarst - literally 'ancient karst'; karst that formed many millions of years ago and was buried by later deposition of rock. *(p 11; fig 28)*

paragenesis - a process of cave formation in which passages enlarge upwards and/or outwards by solution because their floors are protected from dissolution by sediment deposits. *(p 21; figs 12, 14, 19 & 26)*

photokarren (photokarst) - light-orientated karst features formed by the interaction of endolithic algae (living within the surface layer of the rock) with limestone. *(pp 16 & 29)*

phreatic - below the water table. *(p 18; fig 12)*

phreatic tube/half-tube - tube-like cave passage formed below the water table by equal dissolution of roof, walls and floor. *(p 20; figs 12, 17, 27 & 28)*

rillenkarren - narrow, sharp-edged solution grooves which form on steep limestone faces. *(p 14; fig 7)*

rinnenkarren - rather broad, rounded-edged solution runnels which form on more gently sloping limestone. *(p 14; Front Cover)*

rising (resurgence or spring) - the point where an underground stream emerges at the surface again. *(p 18; figs 12, 34 & 38)*

scallops - asymmetric, scoop-shaped hollows formed by water flowing over a soluble rock. *(p 21; figs 15 & 19)*

schist - a foliated or flakey type of metamorphic rock common in Connemara.

shale - mudstone which has been compressed to form a thinly layered, or laminated, rock. Shale is impervious to water, which instead flows on the surface. *(p 7)*

sink (swallow hole) - the point where a stream passes underground. *(p 18; fig 12)*

slickenside - scratches formed by two rock masses moving past each other on a fault. *(pp 12 & 43; fig 27)*

stalactites - straw-shaped or tapering masses of calcium carbonate deposited on a cave roof by percolating water. *(p 22; fig 16)*

stalagmites - often rounded or conical masses of calcium carbonate deposited on a cave floor by dripping percolation water. *(p 22; fig 16)*

steephead - the abrupt, and usually steep-walled, head of a valley which lies behind some risings or springs. *(p 56)*

tufa - a rather porous form of calcium carbonate often deposited by small springs in limestone regions. *(p 45)*

turlough - literally 'dry lake'; a seasonal lake in which both inlet and outlet are underground. *(p 14; figs 22, 35, 36, 37 & Back Cover)*

uvala - term used for large and complex dolines. *(p 14 & 36; fig 24)*

vadose - above the water table. *(p 20; fig 12)*

vadose canyon/trench - a trench or canyon-like passage formed by a cave stream cutting down into a passage floor in the vadose zone. *(p 20; figs 12, 13 & 16)*

vadose shaft - a vertical cave passage formed by a cave stream falling down a fracture under gravity. *(p 20; fig 12)*